It had been concern for her mother, and no other reason, that had made Suzanne refuse to go abroad with Ross Beckett whom she had loved so dearly—but as a result, he had left her in anger and bitterness and she had not seen him since. Now, six years later, he was back. But how could she ever expect him to forgive her?

## Books you will enjoy
### by LILIAN PEAKE

### PASSIONATE INTRUDER

'No man is an island,' Sharon Mason had reminded Calum Calder—to which he had replied firmly, 'This man is.' So she had better not let herself fall in love with him, had she? Especially as he persisted in believing all those lying stories about her . . .

### HEART IN THE SUNLIGHT

Norway, Noelle found when she went to work there, was a land of sunlight, glorious scenery and charming people—with the exception, unfortunately, of her boss, the infuriating Per Arneson!

### STAY TILL MORNING

Who but a heartless monster like Brent Napier would callously turn a girl out of the only home she had? Linette thought bitterly. And having turned her out, couldn't he be content with that? Why did he have to keep interfering in her personal affairs as well?

### THE SUN OF SUMMER

On an enthralling holiday cruising down the Rhine, Marilyn couldn't be sure whether it was being made or marred by the attractive but mysterious Blair Barron. If only she could be sure how he really felt about her!

# NO OTHER MAN

BY

LILIAN PEAKE

MILLS & BOON LIMITED
15–16 BROOK'S MEWS
LONDON W1A 1DR

*First published 1982*
*Australian copyright 1982*
*Philippine copyright 1983*
*This edition 1983*

© Lilian Peake 1982

ISBN 0 263 74108 7

*Set in Monophoto Times 10 on 10½ pt.*
*01–0283 – 59135*

*Made and printed in Great Britain by*
*Richard Clay (The Chaucer Press) Ltd,*
*Bungay, Suffolk*

# CHAPTER ONE

How many times, Suzanne wondered as she combed her hair, would she need to go out with Miles Harringdon before she learned not to flinch each time he touched her?

As many years, she answered herself, as it would take her to forget the only man to whom she had ever given herself, body and soul. And for as long as it took before she ceased to be haunted by the sight of that man walking down that road and out of her life.

Every time she went out with Miles, her mother urged, 'Be nice to him, dear. One day he might propose, then wouldn't it be wonderful?'

Propose what? Suzanne would wonder. Wonderful for whom? What a pity, she thought, finding her bag, that parents were so out of step with the generation to whom they had given birth that they didn't seem to understand that nowadays, any 'proposal' from a man might well be not to marry, but to live with him. Not that Miles was that kind of person. He was a conformist to the core.

Descending the stairs, her simply-styled, short-sleeved dress revealing her slim figure, Suzanne heard Miles talking to her father. Her hand, ringless like the other, reached out to open the door. Miles paused in mid-sentence to smile back, then he continued with the discussion.

Her father inspected her as detachedly as he might look over a new piece of furniture being added to the stock of items sold by his furnishing company.

Suzanne was aware that her father, like her mother, was anxious that her friendship with Miles Harringdon would develop into a more permanent relationship. How often had they said to her that, at the age of twenty-three, it was time she looked around for a man to marry who would become her husband and the father of her children?

What would they have said if she'd told them that there was only one man she had ever wanted in her life, but that he had walked out of it? And that there was only one man by whom she wanted children, but that was as impossible as an infant learning to manoeuvre a spacecraft?

The country restaurant to which Miles took her was a good, no-nonsense establishment. The staff knew them well. It was one of Miles' favourite haunts. The lights were not low, no candles flickered as in Miles' father's restaurants, white tablecloths were starched to a stiffness which suited Miles' personality. The one good thing about the place, Suzanne was forced to concede, was the quality of its food.

'It's why I come here so often,' Miles had once explained. 'It's almost as good as ours.'

Now, he smiled at her across the table. He had given their order, knowing her preferences well after their eight-month acquaintance. 'You're looking nice tonight,' he remarked. She smiled her thanks.

He's calling me 'nice', Suzanne thought, shivering mentally. As a word, it was noncommittal and unimaginative – in fact, just like the person who used it. Why hadn't he come straight out with it, she wondered, and called her 'an uncomplicated, ordinary girl' with no hang-ups, no objectives career-wise and, most important of all, no other boy-friends to get in the way.

How little he knows, she reflected, pleating the starched smoothness of her napkin. How little *everybody* knows about me.

'You look nice, too,' she answered, complimenting herself wryly on the brilliance of her conversational technique.

As a statement it was true. His tweedy suit matched the surroundings, his light brown hair dressed—there was no other way to describe it—to enhance the ladder-climbing look.

When Suzanne heard him order a special champagne, she experienced a prickling of her skin. He smiled across at her as if he was in possession of a big secret. As if I didn't know, Suzanne thought, her heartbeats slow but hard.

While awaiting the appearance of the main course, Miles talked about his work. His father, he said, had plans for expansion, moving up the scale to the grander height of the prestige-restaurant level.

When the champagne was poured and the waiter had gone, Miles lifted his glass, paused as though he had forgotten something and put it down. His face glowed in advance of the alcohol and for once, he seemed unable to express his thoughts. 'I—er——' he cleared his throat, 'I have a proposition to make, Suzanne.'

A proposition? As my mother said, Suzanne thought, but from this man, she knew, it would be a proposition of the old-fashioned kind.

His hand extended across the table, grasping hers. She felt the moistness of his palm. Even as he asked her to marry him, she was shaking her head.

'It's very—very——' she wished she could think of a bland enough word, 'kind of you, Miles——'

'Kind? I'm not being kind. I'm asking because I——'

She had not even threatened to interrupt his flow of words, so why had he stopped?

'I'm sorry, but the answer's "no".' She accompanied the refusal with a smile.

He released her hand and carefully rotated his glass by its stem. He looked crestfallen but, she perceived with a surprise, he also looked worried. Then his padded shoulders lifted. 'Ah, well, I'll try again. I mean it, Suzanne.'

'Try again by all means, Miles, but you won't make me change my mind. We're so different. I'm not the right person for you, you know.'

There's only one man I'm right for, she thought, and he doesn't want me, hasn't wanted me for six years now, not since I was seventeen and he—and he was twenty-four.

She picked up her glass. 'Let's drink, anyway, Miles. To your future, and—and may you find your father's chair comfortable when he retires from the top position of his company.'

Miles blushed and smiled. 'To—to our future together,' he said doggedly. 'I mean it, Suzanne.'

She made an I-can't-stop-you movement with her shoulders and drank with him.

Miles dropped her outside her parents' house. For the first time, he refused her invitation to join them over a hot drink. As he drove away, she walked slowly to the front door. She was engulfed by a sense of release.

The moment she entered the house, the television was switched off. There was a feeling of waiting. What were they expecting, Suzanne wondered, peeling off her summerweight coat, how much did they know?

A great deal, it seemed, from their expressions. Her mother's thin face was smiling, her shadowed eyes bright as they probed beyond her daughter's back. 'Miles is in the hall?' she asked.

'Come on, lad,' her father's voice boomed, his full-cheeked face smiling knowingly, 'no need to be shy. Here, lass,' her father hadn't spoken so pleasantly to her for many years, 'show us the ring.'

'You know?' Suzanne asked, clasping her hands at her waist.

'Of course we know,' her father said. 'Didn't Miles ask my permission while he was waiting for you? And didn't he show us the ring-box?'

So he'd had a ring, anticipating her acceptance of him? He'd also asked her father's permission? Yes, it went with his character.

'Suzanne, dear?' Her mother's voice held a faint waver. 'He did propose, didn't he?'

'If you mean did he ask me to marry him, yes, Mother, he did.'

'Well?' her father demanded. Suzanne stayed silent. 'You don't mean——' there was a frightening edge to the thickening voice, 'you *refused* him?'

So often in the past, Lucas Cannon had been able to cow his wife, but he had never managed to browbeat his daughter. Such a time was now. Suzanne straightened her shoulders, lifted her head high.

'I refused him, Father.'

As if he couldn't believe the statement, Lucas reached out and grabbed his daughter's left hand. No ring met the stare of disbelief in his bloodshot eyes.

His fist clenched, lifted and caught Suzanne a glancing blow on her arm, making her stagger. Her chin trembled, but her eyes glared back into his.

'You haven't changed,' she said, her voice low, 'the years have made you worse, not better. But too bad for you, Father—I've got a great deal of you in my character. You won't get the better of me.'

She swung to the door, her hands gripping each other so hard they hurt.

'Suzie,' her mother's appealing whisper followed her. She swung round, never able to resist her mother's cry for help.

'Let her go, Cynthia. Let the ungrateful little——'

The slam of the door behind Suzanne cut off his words.

In her bedroom, Suzanne stared into the darkness. Only a faint trembling would have told an onlooker of her distress.

A face stared back at her. It was her own, but with seven years stripped away. At sixteen, she'd been hopelessly in love. He was not a boy, the man she had loved. He had not matched her uncertain girlhood with a reciprocal inexperience.

Ross had been his name, Ross Beckett. She had loved him with a passion that was fully and completely adult. He had been seven years older. His crime, in her parents' eyes, had been that he had no money. Poverty, to her father both then and now, equalled criminality. It was better, her father had often said, to be dead than poor.

There was the faintest tap on wood, and Suzanne stiffened. Her father? How could it be? He would have hammered, demanding entry. Suzanne went across and turned the key, opening the door. The pale, worried face of her mother gazed up at her, her spare frame making Suzanne's heart ache.

Even the good quality clothes could not disguise her mother's thinness. The gold and diamond rings were meant to look rich and beautiful, not to weigh down the frail fingers that wore them. Yet her mother was only in her fifties.

Yes, her mother was poor—not in material things. She was rich in those. But they did not nourish her emotions nor give a radiating warmth to her heart. It was love she needed, and from the man to whom she was married. He did not realise how truly poverty-stricken his wife was. The irony would have made Suzanne smile if it had not been her mother who was being so deprived.

Suzanne locked the door and put her back to it.

'Don't worry,' her mother said, 'he won't come looking. He's gone out.'

'To the pub?' Her mother nodded. 'To drink himself silly, I suppose. Then you'll be the one he hits out at.'

Suzanne put her arms round the thin frame. 'Mother, I can't bear to see you suffer. Leave him. Come with me. I'll find a place. I've got some savings, and I could sell the jewellery Father's given me.' Instead of love, she almost added.

Her mother sank to the bed. 'No, no, I could never leave your father, dear. However could you think it? He needs me—he always has.'

'To shout at, to abuse.'

'Only with words, Suzie, only with words.'

Suzanne shook her head helplessly, sitting beside her mother and taking a heavily-veined hand in hers. 'I'm—I'm sorry to cause you all this trouble, Mother, but I couldn't—I just couldn't marry Miles.' For so many reasons I couldn't, she thought. Her mother's hand started shaking even as her daughter held it.

'You've got to marry Miles, Suzie dear, you've got to!'

'But I——' Suzanne took a breath. 'Tell me why, Mum, just tell me why I've got to marry a man I can't look up to, let alone love.'

Her mother put her free hand to her head. 'I'll have to tell you, although Lucas told me not to. You know Miles' father is Bill Harringdon?'

'Of Harringdon's Restaurants? Yes, of course I know that.'

'Well then, don't you understand?'

Suzanne smiled. Her mother always did think that people could read her mind. 'I understand what their business is. They're expanding, Miles told me this evening, spreading across the country. You know, sales talk before he proposed.' Her mother did not see her joke.

'That's the point, dear.'

Suzanne released her mother's hand, finding the shaking had been passed on to her own. 'What's the point?'

'Your father's furniture business—it's doing badly. The sales are going downhill. We—we need money to keep it going. An injection of cash, or something, your father called it.'

Suzanne stood up, crossing her arms and gripping her own elbows. 'Which means that Father wanted me to marry Miles and then he could ask Miles' father for financial assistance?'

'Yes, yes.' Her mother was smiling now. 'Unite the two families, then ask Bill Harringdon for help. Now do you understand?'

I understand all right, Suzanne thought, clenching her teeth. I also understand just how unscrupulous my father is.

Cynthia rose, putting an imploring hand on her daughter's arm. 'So will you think about it, dear, think about Miles' proposal? He's a nice boy, Suzie. He's got money. He'll look after you, like your father looked after me.'

Suzanne stared at her mother. Did she really mean

what she was saying? After the way her husband had treated her through all their years of marriage?

'Mum, Mum,' she covered her face, 'I don't know, I just don't know.' There was so much her mother did not know, too.

'Suzanne, for my sake, will you say yes to Miles?' The frail hand gripped Suzanne's arm. 'If you refuse, my life won't be worth living, dear.'

Oh God, Suzanne thought, what am I to do? She was caught in a trap which she herself had set seven years ago, when she was only sixteen. At that age, how could she have known what she was doing? How could anyone, no matter how old or how young, see that far into the future?

At breakfast, Suzanne had to force herself to meet her mother's pleading gaze.

Keep the peace, her mother was telling her silently, don't quarrel with your father.

Lucas Cannon sat bulkily over his breakfast in the morning-room, the *Financial Times* forming a pink and impenetrable barrier to family irrelevances. The only world that was real to him was the world of commerce and finance.

He had not glanced at his daughter all the time she had been at the table. Cynthia served the meal, refusing Suzanne's offer of help. 'You're going to work, both of you,' she pampered, implying in her self-effacing way that being a simple housewife was, by comparison, of no consequence.

'Call what she does work?' Lucas lowered the newspaper and glared at his daughter. 'Hanging around all day in a shop selling bits and pieces of basketwork?'

Suzanne pushed back her chair, gave her father the benefit of her blazing eyes, then thanked her mother for the meal. Picking up her shoulder bag, she turned at the door.

'See you this evening, Mum.' Then she was on her way. That day, she was in sole charge of the shop. The owner and senior assistant, Maggie Millet, was in the north of England looking out for new lines.

Trade was slack for a while and Suzanne retreated into a corner to continue with her weaving of a series of table mats. At first, the work absorbed her, but she found her mind wandering. Beneath the surface of her life, things were happening. Even now they were breaking through the surface calm.

Her father's furniture manufacturing company was in trouble and he was all set to use her as the key to the solution of the problem. Too bad that his plans were doomed from the start, she thought. Too bad for him that she had inherited his obstinacy and strength of will.

There was a time, seven years back, when she had hated the very thought of him. He'd been able to make her cry in those days, arouse her to near-hysteria by his callous treatment of her adolescent self. She had fallen in love with a young man—not even a boy of her own age, her father had dismissed.

They had met at a discothèque. She had gone with a school friend. Her name, Suzanne recalled, was Bridget. They had seen him simultaneously. 'I'm going to get him,' Bridget had said.

'How?' Suzanne had asked, envying her her superior knowledge of the ways of sprawling young men who were so tall and big they spilled over from the hard-backed chairs and eyed the girls with a certain stomach-clutching look in their eyes.

'Go and ask him to dance, that's how.' And Bridget had, presenting herself with uplifted brows and a swing of her hips.

The young man had been quick to accept her offer, Suzanne had noticed. She saw that he was watching his partner's movements with a strange look that revealed both a sexual excitement and a worldly cynicism which had Suzanne wishing with all her young heart that she were the object of that look.

When the dance ended, he'd walked Bridget back. Bridget had not released his hand. 'My—my friend,' she'd been forced to say. 'Her name's Suzanne. What's yours?' She gazed up at him, but he did not answer. His eyes were on Suzanne, but their expression was very different now.

Suzanne had smiled and smiled, but she was thinking unhappily, Why can't I make him look at me like he looked at Bridget?

The music started again. His hand came out, not towards Bridget, but to Suzanne. He's being kind, she had thought, giving me a dance as well as my friend.

The lights had been lowered, the dancing area filled. 'It's a slowie,' Suzanne had commented. 'I'm not sure I——'

'I'll show you,' he'd said. And show her he did, pulling her against him. 'Arms round my neck,' he had instructed. Round his neck they had curled. 'Move exactly in time with me—not like that, like this.' His hands had moved from her waist to her hips, pressing her so near she could feel the muscle-movement of his thighs.

At first, she had tried to pull away, but after a few moments she had begun to enjoy the new sensations, the hardness of a man touching her and making her body burn.

His face—she wanted to see his face. Her head went back and his lips had caught hers, blotting out the world. Then his eyes were dancing with laughter, making her lip quiver.

'I can't help it,' she'd said, 'if I don't know the rules.'

'Your friend does.'

'So what? She's more experienced.'

'At seventeen?' His smile had broadened.

'Sixteen, same as me.'

A frown had come and gone from his face as her eyes drank in his features. A mouth that made her want to reach up with hers, eyebrows that were marked darkly, and his eyes—in the moving, coloured lights she could not tell their colour. His hair was dark, his chin square— there was so much about him that she liked! *And he was so sexy*. If only . . . if only she had the power to make him look at her as he'd looked at Bridget.

'What's your name?' he'd asked her, 'Suzanne what?'

'Cannon,' she had told him. 'What's yours?' It was suddenly imperative that she should know.

'Ross, Ross Beckett. Satisfied?'

She had nodded and felt strangely content.

'I'm not letting you go,' he'd said as the dance had ended. 'You're going to be my partner until the evening's over.'

Suzanne had gasped. 'I can't stay that late. My father would kill me!'

'You're joking.'

'Well, a bit, but I meant he'd shout and wave his arms about and my mother would cry.'

'What a family! I'll have to take you away from them.'

She had grinned up at him. 'Now you're joking.'

If only she had known then how far from joking he had really been . . . The door bell summoned her to the shop. Putting aside the mat she had hardly touched, she went to serve the woman who had entered.

That evening, all the while Suzanne was in her father's presence, there seemed to be a state of armed truce between them. Now and then she caught her mother's imploring look, saying, Don't start anything, *please*.

Her smile, each time, seemed to reassure her mother. While the television was on, her father sat at the antique bureau, working on papers. Suzanne felt relatively relaxed while his back was to them and was able to lose herself in the play.

When it was over, her father went out. Her mother leant forward in the armchair. 'Suzie? If Miles phones, you will go out with him, won't you?'

'Mother, he won't phone. I turned him down flat.' Her mother's face paled. 'But—but if he does,' Suzanne added hurriedly, 'yes, I'll go out with him, if only to see you looking cheerful again.'

Cynthia's colour returned. She smiled, leaned back and closed her eyes. Lucas came back and, book in hand, occupied the other armchair. Suzanne rose from the couch.

'Don't let me drive you out,' her father's voice said caustically.

'You did that long ago, Father,' Suzanne heard herself replying. At once she regretted having spoken the words.

'Will you two stop trying to score points off each other,' Cynthia pleaded.

'I was going up to my room, anyway,' Suzanne replied, bent to kiss her mother's cheek and left her parents alone.

All week there was no telephone call from Miles. Suzanne was beginning to believe he really could take no for an answer when he rang.

'It's Miles,' her mother said excitedly, holding out the phone. She retreated to the doorway of the living-room, and stood there.

'Forgiven you?' she heard her daughter say. 'For what? Oh, not calling earlier. I'm sure you've been busy. So have I. Tomorrow evening? Well, I——' She heard a cut-off gasp from the doorway. 'Yes, I can manage that. Seven? We'll eat out? Yes, it would be nice. Thanks. See you here tomorrow.'

Even as the receiver clicked into place, she heard her mother's whispered, 'Thank you, Suzie dear.'

Suzanne was buttoning the blouse she intended to wear under her blue tailored two-piece suit. She had resolutely decided against making herself look in the least attractive to Miles, since she wanted to do nothing to make him feel she was encouraging him to take his relationship with her on to a more intimate level.

A whispering voice outside asked, 'May I come in, dear?'

'No need to knock, Mother,' Suzanne called. Cynthia entered, looked at the cluttered chair and opted for the bed.

'You're looking very sweet, Suzie dear,' she commented.

Suzanne started to shake her head, then stopped. Why not let her mother dream her dreams about Miles and herself? Putting down the comb, she met her own reflected eyes in the mirror. The lack of make-up made her look pale, but this pleased her, since it might make her appear less attractive to Miles.

Nothing, however, could take away the character in the large brown eyes which held more than a hint of unhappiness, nor the chestnut lights in her brown hair. The high cheekbones she had inherited from her mother, but there was no doubting that the rounded jawline and stubborn chin had come straight from her father.

Suzanne did not know whether she resented having so much of her father in her. There were many things he was and she was not. Unscrupulous, self-opinionated and blustering—these were characteristics which belonged just to him. Nor could she forget the way he had behaved seven years ago, treating her and the man she had loved in a way that still horrified her to think of it.

'This evening, Miles might—just might propose,' her mother was saying.

Suzanne did not answer, continuing to fix stud earrings in her ears.

'If he does, dear, will you accept?' Cynthia persisted. Receiving no reply, she came to stand beside her daughter. 'Suzie, promise me you'll accept!' The strain was in her voice, the tension apparent in her stiff, frail body.

Suzanne turned to her mother. 'I can make no promises, none at all.'

'For me, dear, for my sake!' Cynthia was whispering now, grasping her daughter's sleeve. Still Suzanne shook her head.

'Not for anyone's sake.' Suzanne covered her eyes, concentrating her thoughts and coming to a decision. 'You want to know why, Mum, you really want to know?' Cynthia was nodding, letting her daughter lead her back to the bed. 'Then I'll tell you. But take a hold, Mum. It's going to shock you.'

Cynthia stared up at her daughter, looking so childlike that Suzanne wanted to put her arms round her.

'Mother,' Suzanne took a breath, 'I'm already married.'

# CHAPTER TWO

FOR a moment, Suzanne thought her mother was going to faint. Her eyes fluttered and closed, but she did not crumple. When she opened them again, they held a blank look.

'No, no, Suzanne, you can't be!' Her mother's head was moving from side to side. 'You've never had a steady boy-friend ... except——' She stared at her daughter. 'Except *him*.'

'Ross Beckett. Yes, Mother. I married Ross Beckett.' She sat beside her mother.

'But how? When? He asked your father, but he said no, he wouldn't let you marry a——'

'Poverty-stricken student, with no background, no guts and only enough intelligence to be a delivery boy, a railway porter and collector of used dishes from café tables. I remember, Mother, only too well. He'd been all those things, he'd had to, to earn enough to keep his mother and himself and save up to pay for himself to go to university.'

'Did he tell your father that?'

'Father wouldn't listen, wasn't interested. Anyway, Father said I was too young to marry.' All right, he said, so his daughter was in love. It wouldn't take her long to fall out of it again at her age, especially as her boy-friend was seven years older than she was.

Suzanne stood up, clasping her hands to stop them from trembling. 'But I married him, Mother, I did become his wife.'

'You couldn't at that age without your parents' consent, dear.'

'We applied to the court for consent and they gave it. The marriage was completely valid, Mum.'

'It wasn't because you were——pregnant?'

'No, it was because we loved each other so much,' Suzanne's voice wavered, 'we could hardly bear to be apart. Ross had his principles, strong ones. He wanted me as his wife, not a semi-permanent girl-friend, he said.'

'You didn't live with him, Suzie. You lived here.'

'Yes, but you remember the times I told you I was going to stay with Bridget, or my other school friends? Well, I didn't, Mum. I stayed with Ross, in his room at the house he shared with other students.'

'But, Suzie,' Cynthia still seemed to be trying to find ways of disproving her daughter's claim, 'you don't wear a wedding ring.'

'I did when I went to stay with Ross. Other times, I kept it tucked away.' She sat beside her mother again. 'I've still got it tucked away, and our marriage certificate, too.'

There was a long pause. 'Where is Ross now?' Cynthia asked, staring at her clasped hands.

'I don't know. I haven't known his whereabouts since the day—the day he walked away from me.' Suzanne put a hand to her face in a gesture of despair. 'We'd quarrelled, you see. He got his degree—he only had one more year to go when we were married. He qualified as a geologist. He'd got himself a job with an oil company. The head office was in this country, but his work involved going overseas to Africa and so on. He wanted me to go with him, and I said I couldn't.'

After a long while, her mother asked, 'Why didn't you, Suzanne?'

'Why?' She could not tell her mother the reason, she couldn't say she had thought that by staying, she could act as a barrier between her mother and her father, parrying his verbal onslaughts on her mother, taking them herself because she was the stronger.

The few moments which had led up to the final parting returned and every memory was like a knife-thrust. 'I can't leave my parents, Ross,' she'd told him. 'My father's a brute, and mother doesn't know how to deal with him. She lets him push her around, walk all over her. I must stay to protect her. Can't you see?' she had asked him in anguish. 'I'm talking about my mother! She's defenceless against him . . .'

'What about me?' he had raged, quite uncomprehending of the depths of her agony. 'I'm the man you married. Doesn't that count for anything? You're seventeen now. Isn't it time you grew up and realised you've got to let go of your parents, let your mother fend for herself? Isn't it time you walked alone in the world—except you won't be alone, because you'll have me?'

'I'm not afraid to walk alone,' she'd answered, hardly able to breathe for the rising tears, 'I'm not afraid for myself, but for my mother.'

Ross had been white around his mouth. His blue eyes had turned almost black with fury. 'Then stay with your mother. But I'm warning you, if you let me go away alone, without you, I'll disappear out of your life for ever.'

'Why, Ross, why?' she had pleaded. 'Why must you go at all? Why can't you stay with me?'

'Why must I go? My God,' he looked at her scathingly, 'you've not only not grown up, you're still a babe in arms! Emotionally, you've only just been born!' He shook her by the shoulders. 'It's my work, my career, it's what I nearly killed myself working for, it's what I qualified to do. Don't you understand, girl, don't you understand?'

Just for a moment, she had seen his point of view. Then the faint glimpse her insight had given her had been completely eclipsed by the remembrance of her mother's paper-white face, her mother's constant tiredness after those battles with her father. 'I can't,' she had whispered miserably.

He had turned on his heel and left her. That was the last time she had seen him. The wedding ring stayed hidden away. The happy hours—so few when Suzanne looked back on them—which they had spent together, were almost worn out with constant recall, but their essence stayed bright in her mind, even after six years of separation.

'You could divorce him, Suzanne.' Her mother's soft voice brought her back to the present. 'A solicitor would help to find him, surely? Then you could start proceedings.'

Divorce him? she wanted to cry. I still love him, so how can I let him go? But he didn't want her. If he had, he would have come back to claim her. He knew where she lived. He probably had another woman who didn't mind that he wasn't legally free. So why should she be sitting there, six years later, still mourning the man who had let her go so easily?

Hadn't he realised that seventeen was not really 'grown up' and that, at that age, she had really thought she could protect her mother? Couldn't he have tried to see her point of view? He himself had been on the receiving end of her father's terrible temper.

Surely he could have tried to put himself in her place as she watched her mother react by shrinking into herself, by going pale, by buckling at the knees as her father had ranted and raged?

At seventeen, she was not to know that not all the youthful idealism in the world, nor all the measured reasoning with a furious-tempered man, would change that man one smallest bit. Look at her mother now. Had her own presence there made her mother's life any more tolerable? What if she had gone with Ross? Hadn't she had her answer when her mother had said the other day that she could never leave the man she had married?

Maybe Ross had known, his extra seven years having given him more knowledge of human nature. In her heart and with hindsight, Suzanne knew she should have gone with him, that he had been in the right. But what use was hindsight? And did it matter any more, anyway? Emotionally and physically, the ties between them had been cut a long time ago.

'If Miles proposes again, Suzie,' her mother's voice

insinuated itself into her thoughts, 'you could accept, then go secretly to a solicitor—not your father's, because he mustn't know. You needn't tell Miles, either, not until you go with him to get the licence. If you say you want a long engagement, Ross could be found and divorce proceedings started. I expect he'll be as anxious as you are to be free.'

Painful though it was to acknowledge the fact, it was probably true. Maybe he had even forgotten what she looked like. In an instant, she herself could summon up his face as he had looked in the past, yet he could have changed so much that she might not recognise him.

Suzanne felt herself weakening. It just might be a way round the difficult circumstances. If accepting Miles' proposal would bring about a situation where her father's financial problems could begin to be solved, then why not say 'yes' to Miles?

The doorbell chimed. 'I'll let him in,' Cynthia said, having watched closely the changing expressions on her daughter's face. 'Your father's out. Will you accept, Suzie, will you?'

She smiled into her mother's pleading eyes. 'I'll think about it, Mum.'

Her mother gave a big sigh and went down the stairs.

It was not Miles who had arrived, it was her father. Suzanne emerged from her bedroom to hear the question, 'I thought Miles was coming to take Suzanne out?'

'Yes, dear,' Cynthia placated, 'we thought it was Miles this time, but it was you.'

Suzanne was halfway down the stairs when her father saw her. 'If he proposes, you accept, do you hear me?' he boomed.

'I hear you,' Suzanne answered, continuing slowly to descend.

'If you say no again, I'll turn you out of the house. Understand me?'

'Lucas, please!' Cynthia pleaded.

'Don't bother, Mum. He's made the threat before.' She was downstairs now, confronting her father. 'Seven years ago, remember? When Ross Beckett came and asked your permission to marry me?' Her mother's gasp did not stop her. 'And you threatened to call the police if he didn't leave the premises?'

'Don't talk to me about that young whipper-snapper. Not a penny to his name, and he had the audacity to think he could marry my daughter!'

The door chimes cast a bright sound over the rancorous quarrel. Cynthia went lightly to the door to welcome the newcomer. Lucas whispered to his daughter, 'Now you accept, or else. Right?' He retreated into his office.

After a few words of greeting, Cynthia left her daughter in the hands of the man who, she was convinced with an unwavering certainty, would one day become her true son-in-law.

Eyes closed, her head resting back in the passenger seat of Miles' car, Suzanne was sighing with relief that the evening was over. He drew to a stop. With Miles following, Suzanne approached the house, turned the key and opened the door.

He helped her with her coat, then kissed her a little nervously on her unresponsive lips. Her father was at the living-room door, having wrenched it open in his eagerness.

'Well?' he asked, looking from one to the other and moving backwards into the room.

Suzanne went across to her mother and thrust out her left hand. 'There it is, Mum. Isn't it a beautiful ring? Look, Father, look at the size of that sapphire, the purity of those diamonds.' Her smile was as brittle as her tone of voice.

'You're engaged, Suzie? To Miles? My little girls's going to be married!' She had to give her father top marks for his acting ability.

'Isn't it wonderful?' Cynthia was saying. 'Oh, Miles, Suzie, you've made us both so happy!'

'Glad you're pleased, Mrs Cannon.' Miles pulled

Suzanne to his side. 'I'm so happy tonight. Suzanne's going to make me a wonderful wife, I know it.'

There's so much you don't know, Suzanne thought, but made her smile match his in brightness.

'Do your parents know, young man?' Lucas asked. 'No? Then I'll get on to them. There'll be so much to do, preparing for the wedding. The engagement mustn't be a long one.'

'We're not in a hurry, Father.' Suzanne's cool words had her father whirling from the telephone. 'We've agreed not to rush things, haven't we, Miles?'

The nod Miles gave was reluctant. 'We thought we'd give the engagement a few months at least. Suzanne wanted it that way, so I agreed.'

For a moment, Lucas seemed nonplussed, then he answered, 'Oh, you'll soon change her mind. A few hugs and kisses from her betrothed and she'll be stamping like a young filly to get on with the wedding. Don't think you can fool a man of the world like me.'

He grabbed the receiver and dialled. 'Get yourself a drink, Miles,' Lucas invited airily. 'Pour one for all of us, while you're about it. Bill? I've got wonderful news. Miles and Suzanne—they're engaged!'

He listened, then said, 'A party? Why not? An announcement? You'll see to it? Good. The quality papers, the lot, as far as I'm concerned. We're two important families, after all. We own a couple of flourishing companies between us. Fine, everything's fine. You? Good, good.' After a few more well-wishing phrases, he rang off.

Miles handed Lucas his drink. 'Come on, all of you,' Lucas urged. 'Raise your glasses. To the future of our two companies. And to the happy couple.'

Suzanne noted with a wry amusement the order of her father's priorities.

The party was under way. An outside catering firm had been employed, Lucas having refused the services of the engaged man's father's offer of one of his restaurants for the affair.

On principle, he's said. It wouldn't have been fair taking for nothing something which he, as the bride's father, should be paying for. Suzanne, knowing that her father only wanted the marriage to ensure that Miles' father came to the financial aid of his ailing firm, kept her opinion of her father's 'principles' to herself.

At her father's insistence, she had removed the engagement ring and returned it, temporarily, into Miles' keeping. When her father had said he would like a re-enactment of the placing of the ring on her finger, Suzanne had shrugged.

It would be the climax of the evening, he had said, even though the guests would have seen the announcement in the papers three days before.

Suzanne had filled a plate for herself with the enticing savouries on display. As an afterthought, she had repeated the exercise for Miles, knowing it would be a gesture appreciated by the relatives on both sides. To be seen giving her 'fiancé' a plate of food would signify, to them, how much she cared for him.

The action seemed to give the recipient of the plate the same idea. He thanked her by kissing her boldly, and smiled with shining embarrassment at the romantic sighs from all around them.

After a few moments' eating, however, Suzanne found she had lost her appetite. Putting down her half-filled plate, she dusted away the crumbs from her silky blue dress. Around her neck she wore an engraved gold necklace, in her ears matching earrings, all gifts from her father.

She would by far have preferred loving kindness, something which had never come her way from him and probably never would. To this fact she had long ago become reconciled.

There was music from the stereo equipment and dancing was suggested. Miles knew how to dance and their steps matched well. It brought her no pleasure.

She remembered other times and happier days when she had danced in the arms of the only man on earth who had mattered to her.

Others drew back to watch them as they danced. Miles wanted to look into her eyes. This she knew by his whispered, 'Look at me.' She refused to do so, staring instead into space. The glass doors to the patio were open, the evening breeze cooling the atmosphere, but Suzanne was already cold inside.

The music stopped, there was applause and Miles kept her in the centre of the floor. It all seemed to be pre-arranged. Her father stepped forward.

'I've got an announcement to make!' he shouted, although everyone had gone quiet. Suzanne wished he had included her mother in the scene, but knew it was typical of her father that he should take the stage.

'My beautiful daughter Suzanne—who has her mother's beauty and her father's brains,' there was loud laughter and Suzanne wished she could cover her ears, 'and Miles, the handsome son of my best friend, Bill Harringdon, are tonight celebrating their engagement. Miles,' he turned, 'do your stuff, my boy.'

With a flourish, Miles drew the ring from his pocket. He caught Suzanne's hand, pushed the ring on to her wedding finger and put his arms around her. His kiss was long and lingering, and everyone applauded.

Suzanne's eyes were wide open, suffering the pressure of his mouth. Her eyes found the opened doors and she concentrated on the darkness beyond. A movement outside brought her to awareness, and her heart began to pound. A stranger lurked, a tall man, broad and hard-faced. Terror started to rise, bringing a scream to her throat. She tore her lips from Miles'.

The man stepped into the room and the guests swung round.

'Sorry to gatecrash,' he said, his voice deep and resonant, 'and I must apologise for my untidy appear-ance. I've travelled a long way in the last twenty-four hours.'

He looked around at the waiting, frightened faces. His smile was caustic and fleeting.

'I had to come—it was essential.' He stared straight at Suzanne's ashen face. 'I had to stop my wife from committing bigamy.'

# CHAPTER THREE

THERE was a gasping silence, then all eyes swung to Suzanne. Her hand was grasping her throat. 'Ross?' she whispered.

He strolled across the room and the crowd made way as if he were an outcast. He stood in front of Suzanne, his face taut with fatigue, his jaw rigid, blue eyes piercing and full of contempt.

He ran his hands over his brown, unruly hair, then thrust them into his jeans pockets. His brown sweater, with its rounded neck, revealed that he wore no tie. He was as out of place as a beggar at a feast, except that no beggar had his look of reined fury.

'Who else?' He answered Suzanne's question. He looked down at the engagement ring, flung a dismissing glance at her companion. 'Or did you reckon on my having died of some dread disease in the African jungle?'

'What is this,' Bill Harringdon asked, his lined face bewildered, his thin body taut, 'a hoax? Did you lay this on, Lucas? Are we meant to laugh?'

'Who the hell are you?' Miles demanded, electrified into activity by his father's puzzlement.

'Didn't she tell you—even you,' Ross asked, 'the man she conned into offering to *marry* her? I'm her husband.' He lifted Suzanne's hand. 'Where's your wedding ring?'

'Take your hands off my daughter!' Lucas's voice boomed, as he strode across the room. 'Get out of here, and take your lies with you!'

'It's no lie, Father,' Suzanne said tonelessly. 'I married Ross seven years ago.'

'Oh no, you didn't, my girl,' Lucas said nastily. 'The day you both came to me asking my permission because you were under the age of marrying without parental consent, I said no. And I threw him,' with a dismissing sideways movement of his head, 'out of the house.'

'You're good at that, Mr Cannon,' Ross sneered. 'You've threatened me with eviction again tonight. But it's too late.'

Lucas swung to face him. 'What do you mean, too late? If she lied about her age, I'll reveal it in the right quarters and any *marriage* you think you contracted into becomes invalid.'

'I didn't lie about my age, Father. We—Ross and I—sought the permission of the courts to marry. After consideration, they gave permission, and we were married. I've got the marriage certificate to prove it.'

Ross considered her detachedly. 'So you haven't torn it up?'

'Not yet,' she retaliated. 'When I marry Miles, maybe I will.' She stepped closer to her 'fiancé'.

Ross's hand jerked upwards in the direction of Miles, but it was Suzanne who flinched, certain he was going to hit her. There was a murmur from the crowd.

He looked around at the noise, saw the hate on the flushed faces. 'I want you back.'

'She's mine,' Miles declared, holding her arm. 'I'm going to marry her.'

Ross treated the defiant statement with contempt. He gripped Suzanne's shoulder and forcibly removed her from Miles' hold. He jerked her towards him.

'Take your hands off my daughter, you upstart!' Lucas repeated.

Ross ignored that statement, too. 'I want you back,' he said, saying each word clearly, 'and I'm going to get you back, even if I have to move mountains to achieve my object.'

He pushed her away, nodded curtly to Lucas Cannon and went out the way he had come.

Suzanne stared into the empty darkness. She heard like the swish of a distant sea the rising conversation. There was horror and incredulity, even sympathy which she guessed was meant for her, but her ears were deaf to everything but the clamour of her own thoughts.

Go after him, she was telling herself, and her feet

obeyed before her mind could stop them. She whirled through the doorway, ignoring her father's order to return. It seemed that Ross had remembered the garden entrance from the past and was almost there by the time she had caught up with him.

'Ross!'

He stopped without turning. 'Yes?'

'I—I just wanted to say "Hallo again" like—like we used to.' As they had when they had shared his narrow bed in the room he had rented while a student. Hallo again, he would whisper as they had lain face to face, bodies burning with passion, igniting into a roaring fire as they had come together.

He turned slowly, looking at her uplifted face in the moonlight. 'Well, you've said it. Thanks for the thought.' The words were spoken caustically, searing like spilt acid.

Maybe if she stretched out her hand . . . It descended, feather-light, on his covered arm. Did he feel its trembling wonder, the delight of touching him after so many years?

He grasped her hand and flung it down. 'Go back to your lover!'

'He isn't my lover! I swear that's the truth.'

'"She's mine", he said. You're not married to him, you can't be in law. Which means only one thing in the times we live in.'

'I haven't slept with him.' There were tears in her voice, but if Ross heard them they did not even begin to touch him.

'For six years you've remained faithful to me? Don't try to kid me!'

As the moon sailed from behind a cloud bank, Suzanne gazed at his time-carved features. The man she had married was there somewhere, but a worldliness had overlaid him, almost eclipsing the laughing, loving husband to whom she had joyfully and utterly surrendered.

Defeated, not so much by the circumstances as the damage wrought by the passage of time, she turned away. 'Goodbye, Ross,' she whispered into the darkness, and heard his footsteps thrust him forward into the night.

The party was over, the guests had gone. It had not lasted much longer after the whirlwind arrival and departure of the man Lucas Cannon had named 'the interloper' in front of his guests.

Miles had remained, telling his parents he would return later. His presence was plainly an irritation to her father, Suzanne noticed, since she was certain he was fretting to give rein to his fury against her.

The furniture had been pushed back into its proper place and Miles drew Suzanne down beside him on the couch. 'You will marry me, won't you?' he pressed. 'You can divorce your—your—him, can't you? It might take a while, but I'd be willing to wait.'

Lucas stood in front of his daughter, a stiff, stocky figure, his white hair ruffled as if an angry hand had raked it. 'That's one thing you will do at my bidding, madam,' he declared. 'You'll divorce that upstart as soon as the law allows!'

Miles stared at Lucas, startled and just a little intimidated by his bellicose attitude. Suzanne realised that Miles had never seen her father's temper in full spate. What Miles did not know was that his own presence there was acting as a flood barrier.

Cynthia entered quietly and seated herself on the edge of the armchair. 'Don't talk like that to her, Lucas,' she urged. 'You'll drive her the other way. You know she's got your obstinacy.'

'I can tell you what she hasn't got—my common sense. Going against my wishes at sixteen, getting herself wed to a man without two coins to rub together. Now what do you think of your fine husband, eh? He hasn't changed, has he? Scruffy as ever, clothes so disreputable you'd think he'd been digging up the road all day. Which is probably all he's good for!'

Suzanne stood to face her father. 'Are you trying to

force me over to his side? Because if you go on much
longer like this, I'll go back to him.'

Lucas answered through his teeth, 'Over my dead
body you will. There's the man you're going to marry,
after you've divorced that other one.'

'That "other one" is your son-in-law, Father.'

'*Son-in-law?*' Lucas exploded. 'You've got the audacity to call him—*him*,' he stabbed the air in the direction
of the glass doors which had been closed and locked,
'*my son-in-law?*'

Miles, plainly concerned by Lucas's scarlet face, rose
to put a hand on his shoulder. 'Calm down, Mr Cannon.
Getting angry like this won't do you any good.'

Cynthia was by her husband's side in seconds. She
led him to a chair and sat him down. Always, it came to
Suzanne out of nowhere, her mother was by her father's
side. She always would be. The truth came at her making
her stagger mentally.

At seventeen, when she had had to make the choice
of going with Ross or staying with her mother—to *protect* her, she recalled with bitter irony—she had lacked
the ability to recognise her mother's eternal devotion to
the man she had married.

So her own sacrifice had been in vain. She had thrown
away her own chance of happiness, only to see her
mother, all these years later, still clinging to her father,
in need of no protection from him whatsoever. For her
pains, her father had connived to use her by putting her
under a moral obligation to marry a man she did not
love.

'Remember, Father,' Suzanne pressed bitterly, 'I'm
the ace in your pack. If you carry on in the way you're
doing, you'll damage yourself, won't you? And I don't
only mean in health. You've got to play your cards right,
and if you lose your ace, you're lost, too. You see,
Mother told me—everything.'

She looked down at her father's bent figure as he sat,
head in hands. Somewhere inside her there was a small
flare of sympathy. The company he had started and

cherished until it had become as much part of him as
his heart was in danger of failing. But he was treating
her like a piece on a chessboard, moving her into whatever position was best for him. The flare died down and
went out.

After bending to kiss Miles on the cheek as he sat on
the couch, she smiled at her mother and kissed her, too.
At the door, she paused to thank her father for the
party. He looked up and met her eyes.

Hers were as vulnerable as if she were a child again,
longing for his understanding. His were censorious and
unforgiving. Tears moistened Suzanne's eyes, she could
not stop them.

Quickly, she turned away and walked out.

In the days that followed, it was as though Ross had
never returned. There was no letter, no call from him.
She knew nothing about him, he had not told them
where he was living, nor whether he had returned to
Nigeria, from which country, he had claimed, he had
rushed at short notice.

How had he known? she wondered. Who had told
him about her 'engagement' to Miles Harringdon? After
a while, Suzanne had begun to wonder if she had
imagined it all. Of course she had not. There had been
so many witnesses to his return.

Since the silence from him had been so prolonged—
five weeks had passed—Miles had started to question
her as to whether she had really married Ross Beckett
all those years ago. Was it valid? he had asked. When
she had shown him the marriage certificate, he had been
convinced.

He was continually urging her to visit a solicitor with
a view to starting divorce proceedings. In the end, she
did so, but when the solicitor heard that she did not
know the whereabouts nor the employers of her husband, he said he foresaw some delay before any positive
move could be taken.

'We have to find your husband, you see,' he said. 'Do
you wish me to institute proceedings in that respect?'

Suzanne hesitated before answering. I need more time, she wanted to tell him. I love the man he used to be, but the man he has become—he frightens me.

In the end, she told the solicitor she would think about it and contact him in a few days. When she went for a meal with Miles that evening, he told her she should have agreed. What he did not seem to understand was that finding Ross would mean that she would have to see him again. This was something she had come to dread increasingly as the days had passed.

In her dreams, their reunion had shown her a vision of unparalleled happiness, an abandoning of all restraint and an encircling of arms so tight that neither could ever escape again from the other.

Reality had been so heartbreakingly different that she wanted to tear the memory of it from her mind. He had altered so much and in so many ways he had become like a stranger.

One evening about six weeks later, Suzanne had taken a call, expecting it to be Miles. When she heard the voice that spoke to her, she closed her eyes and sat down shakily on the chair next to the telephone.

'Yes, it's Suzanne,' she answered, with commendable composure.

'I want to see you,' Ross stated flatly. 'Meet me at the end of your road. My car's a BMW, silver-blue.'

'I'm sorry, but I don't want to see you.'

There was a pause and the fear took hold that he would ring off, but he spoke again. 'Okay, no divorce, which is what I assume you want.'

He had her cornered. 'At the end of the road,' she answered, 'in fifteen minutes.'

'Make it ten.'

Suzanne took a deep breath. 'Ten,' she snapped, and rang off.

The door closed behind her on a quiet house. Her father was out, her mother next-door with her friend. Suzanne was thankful that no explanations had been necessary. The meeting wouldn't last long, she had calculated, which meant that she might even be back before her mother returned.

Suzanne wore a pale pink dress with short sleeves, bow-tied neck and matching belt. It fitted closely, showing her slim but shapely figure to advantage. Her red-brown hair was caught by the breeze and pushed forward to hug her cheeks. In her ears she wore silver earrings—another gift from her father. Her white sandals clicked on the pavement as she moved towards the impressively large parked car along the street.

With each step forward, her heart seemed to take a step down. When she was about two-thirds of the way along the road, the driver's door swung open and Ross got out, moving round the back of the car to the pavement to await her arrival. For the rest of the way, his eyes did not leave her.

Embarrassment tightened her up at the way his gaze skirted over her every contour. Even her legs did not escape the scrutiny. His expression gave nothing away as she endeavoured to return his appraisal, but she could not find the courage to look at him as boldly as he had looked at her.

One glance was enough to tell her how maturity had added another and exciting dimension to his looks. He had broadened in shoulder and chest, his hips and thighs seemed to be made of solid muscle beneath the well-cut casual brown slacks. A leather belt sat low, telling of a lean and toughened build only partly hidden under the brown and white check shirt, opened at the neck. Over it he wore a brown jacket.

'Scruffy', her father had called him. He should see him now, she thought. His smile was sardonic as she stood in front of him. 'You made it,' he commented with sarcasm. 'You must want that divorce badly to have agreed to meet me.'

'When your arm is twisted verbally,' she replied tartly, 'it hurts just as much as the real thing.'

'So you love the man whose ring you're still wearing.' Ross lifted his shoulders, then saw her into the car.

'It's big,' she commented as he settled beside her, fixing his safety belt and indicating that she should do the same. 'Have you hired it while you're home?'

'Hired it?' He fired the engine and moved on. 'No, I bought it about four weeks ago.'

'Was it worth buying a car? I mean, you'll be going back to Africa soon to your oil-drilling, won't you, so——?'

'I was offered a desk job by the company,' he answered quietly. 'Promotion to a high position, good money and in London.'

He wouldn't be going away again? Suzanne panicked, pulling her lightweight jacket more firmly round her shoulders. He would be in London, within easy reach, not only invading her dreams at night but haunting her thoughts by day.

'Would you like a meal?' he asked, gazing ahead.

'No, thanks. I've eaten.'

'We'll go to my hotel, then. I'm staying in the area for a few days. There's a bar, somewhere to talk.'

What did he want to talk about? she wondered, as he parked and switched off the engine. About the divorce? Had he changed his mind about getting her back, even moving mountains? If he had, it would make things so much easier. Not that she would marry Miles. But one day, maybe, someone else . . .

'Do you want me to bring the drinks out here?' The mocking question tugged her back to the present. Ross came round to open the door for her. Since when had his manners been so polite? The rebel in her rejected the cool politeness. She was his wife, not a chance acquaintance.

A man didn't have to make an impression on the woman he had married. If he'd hauled her out, laughing, holding her when she collapsed into his arms—that would have been spontaneous and natural. And wonderful.

Entering the reception area, Suzanne thought, He's surely not going to invite me up to his room? I couldn't bear it. He glanced at her and smiled without amusement. He had plainly read her mind.

'Let me take your jacket.'

More politeness! 'No, thanks,' she answered, gripping it in case he took it away. Her poise was ill-balanced, she had to have something to hang on to.

'This way.' His hand cupped her elbow and she managed to suppress a shiver at his touch. His hold soon dropped away, as if he couldn't bear the feel of her.

The bar was semi-circular, the glass tankards, suspended from a row of high-placed hooks glinted red and yellow in the lights' glow. Stools were lined up at the counter, but Ross led her to a corner settee with its own oval-shaped table. Suzanne sat down, eyeing a chair longingly. Ross removed his coat and found a hook for it.

As a red-jacketed waiter approached, Ross lowered himself to sit beside her. He asked what she would like, then ordered for both of them. He leaned back, seeming disinclined to make conversation. Suzanne could hardly bear his remoteness. Talking would at least remind him that he was not alone.

'How did you——' she cleared her throat of an unexpected huskiness, 'know about me—us? Miles and myself, I mean.' He was in no hurry to answer. 'Our engagement, Ross?'

As she spoke his name, his head turned slowly. 'It was in all the daily papers, wasn't it?'

'Was it? I didn't know. I heard my father tell Mr Harringdon to let the world know.'

'He certainly did that. Where I was working, in deepest Africa, papers arrive a few days late. I rang Head Office in London and told them I was bringing my return forward—I was coming back anyway—because I'd just seen an announcement which seemed to imply that my wife, from whom I was unofficially separated, was about to take unto herself a second husband, before getting rid of the first.'

'I suppose they laughed.'

'They did. They didn't believe me, thought I was joking.'

Their drinks were served. Ross picked up his, motioning to Suzanne that she should do the same. He did not lift his glass high. There was nothing to which to drink a toast.

Conscious of the touch of his thigh against hers, Suzanne shifted slightly. Ross looked at her leg, then at her face. His was completely serious. He was making no effort to entertain her as he would any other invited guest. Leaning back and taking small drinks, feeling her lips trembling a little against the glass, Suzanne told herself he seemed to have lost all feeling.

He made a movement and Suzanne glanced at him, immediately on the alert, but he had merely rested his head back. There was a bitterness about those well-shaped lips she had once nibbled at to arouse him, dancing tiny kisses across them until he reached out and twisted her under him.

He was so remote now she wondered if any woman would be able to penetrate to the sea of emotions inside him, hidden away like a deep pool in an underground cave. Or had his emotional pool dried up, evaporating in the heat of the jungle into which he had plunged after their break-up?

'Why did you want to see me, Ross?'

He leaned forward, putting down his empty glass and waiting while she did the same. 'To ask a few questions.' He looked her over. 'To try to discover what made you forget you had a husband to the extent of becoming quite falsely engaged to another man.'

'I—hadn't forgotten your existence. I had every intention of starting divorce proceedings. After the engagement party, I went to the solicitor, but he told me to discover your whereabouts so that he could proceed.'

'Now you know where I am, you'll rush back tomorrow to see the man?'

He spoke so objectively and coldly, she shivered.

'Yes.' She hadn't thought about it, but she supposed she would. What was the use of staying married to him? He didn't love her any more, that was plain from his every look and word.

'Do you love this man Harringdon?'

Of course she didn't, but she couldn't tell him that! 'What use is love,' she demanded, turning on him, 'when it only brings heartbreak and misery?'

Ross contemplated her flushed face and unhappy eyes. 'You're referring, I suppose, to the day I left you?' She sat silent and he leaned back. 'It fits. You were young enough then to have romantic ideas about the enduring nature of sexual passion, which you probably called "love". So my leaving would have upset you deeply, for a time. You're enlightened enough now, I take it, to enter into the marriage contract for the second time with no illusions about so-called love?'

He was trampling in hobnailed boots over her cherished dreams. *She was crying out inside, I was in love with the man I married and that love has lasted all these years—until now, when I just don't know what I feel.*

*You bear so little resemblance to that young man you used to be, that if I'd been blindfolded when you came through those doors during the party I wouldn't have known you—except for your voice, and even that has deepened in quality.*

Her voice was dull as she asked, 'Do you want to know why I agreed to marry Miles when the divorce was through? It was my father's wish. His company's doing badly and he's hoping to get financial help from the Harringdon company which owns a restaurant chain, by linking the two businesses by means of the marriage.'

Ross did not react to the explanation.

'Which,' Suzanne went on, 'probably proves you're right in your assumption that I no longer have any illusions about romantic love.'

'You mean you're going to let your father use you to further his business ambitions? I'm surprised, consider-

ing the rebel you once were where his wishes were concerned.'

'I'm still a rebel. I'd only be doing it for my mother's
sake.'

His hand rested on her knitted jacket which lay between them. She wanted to put her hand over his but
stopped the thought in its tracks. She could make no
gesture towards this distant-eyed stranger which spoke
even remotely of a feeling of affection.

'I've heard those words somewhere before,' Ross
commented dryly. 'When I asked you to come abroad
with me. No, you said, you couldn't—for your mother's
sake.' He spoke the words derisively.

'All right, you've made your point. So I'm to blame
for the break-up of our marriage. Isn't that what you're
saying?'

His hand lifted, summoning the waiter. He ordered
another drink for himself, asking Suzanne, who shook
her head. In the following moments, there seemed
nothing to say. The waiter returned, accepted the money
and went on his way.

Ross drank for a few minutes, then asked, 'Why can't
your father raise a loan from his bank?'

'I think he's tried, but they refused. The company's in
debt up to its eyes, anyway.'

Ross picked up his glass, his expression thoughtful,
and took another drink.

'I want to see your father,' he said abruptly. He
drained his glass and replaced it with a thump on the
coaster. The movement was a challenge in itself. 'As
soon as possible.'

'He won't see you, Ross. He won't let you into the house.'

'Oh, but he will, my sweet. I'll walk in, with the aid of
your door key.'

Her heart turned over at the endearment, although
she knew it was meaningless.

He stood up, pulling her with him. She scooped up
her cardigan, but he took it from her, hooking it over
his jacket.

'Where are you going?' Suzanne asked, hanging back. 'I refuse to go with you up to your room.'

'I haven't invited you there,' he replied, irony in his smile. He took her with him, his hand still tight round hers. 'There's dancing in one of the public rooms.' He asked a member of the hotel staff and followed the directions.

'I don't want to dance,' Suzanne declared, trying to disentangle her hand.

'Too bad, because I do. After years in the wilds of the jungle, I'm easing myself back to the pleasantries of civilisation, this time by way of a primitive activity— dancing. For that I need a partner.' His smile mocked again. 'And what better partner can I find than my lawful wedded wife?'

'I'm not your——'

'Oh, but you are, Suzanne.' They had reached a room where tables were grouped around a cleared and uncarpeted space. The lights were subdued, the small band winning the battle with the raised and laughing voices.

Ross did not bother to look for a table. Suzanne found herself being pulled straight on to the floor between the other dancers. The dance was romantic and slow. He put her opposite him.

'Dance as we did the first time we met.'

Suzanne shook her head. 'That was different.'

'Do as I say,' he ordered, each word distinct. His hands linked round her waist, her arms, moved upward to cross and rest lightly on his neck. Her body was stiff with a painful tension, resisting the pull of him as their limbs touched in movement.

His eyes ensnared hers, but there was no smile in them. Her breath was coming more easily now, her body growing more pliant. The music was seeping into her, telling her to take with welcoming arms even the smallest fragment of happiness which this man might offer.

Her eyes closed so as to savour the joy of being close to him again. A pressure against her hair told her that his cheek had found a soft resting place and her heart sang. The feel of his lips on hers took her by surprise.

The breathlessness returned, her lips would not give. Ross grew impatient and eased her into a dark corner.

His arms were round her and he had prised her lips apart. He was kissing her in the way he had kissed her so often in the first year of their marriage. But there was something else, a new insistence stemming from an experience of loving that was beyond her.

When he stopped, Suzanne was drained. Her body was shaking with each heavy throb of her pulse. Her cheek lay against the muscled wall of his chest and the feel of him was so different that, for a crazy moment, she questioned whether this man was really her husband, or whether he had changed places with another.

Breaking away, she looked into his face and the light in his eyes told her it was indeed Ross. But he had undergone a character-change so great that the man whose body still pressed against hers put a bewilderment into her mind and a curious fear into her heart.

# CHAPTER FOUR

In the car, Ross asked, 'Will your father be in if I come back with you?'

Any warmth there might have been had gone from him.

Suzanne closed her eyes in despair at the thought of the battle that would lie ahead if she walked into the house with Ross behind her, instead of Miles.

Better to get it over than leave matters unresolved, she decided. 'He might be,' she answered. 'He wasn't in from work when I left the house, so I doubt if he'd go out again this evening.'

Ross nodded and set the car in motion. To Suzanne's relief, he parked his car at the kerb outside the house. His car was bigger than her father's, which would only serve to fan the flames of her father's temper if he were to note the fact. She wondered if Ross possessed discernment enough to have realised this. By his somewhat dry smile as he operated the windows, she knew he had read her mind and had, indeed, known what he was doing.

Waiting for him to move—she had no wish to hurry to the scene of the coming battle—she watched as he switched on an inner light. He took a comb from his inside pocket, running it through his hair.

Turning a crooked smile in her direction, he asked, 'Do I look a little less of an "upstart"?'

Suzanne grinned back and nodded, then turned away quickly to hide the tears which sprang from nowhere. For a precious moment, the old Ross had been there beside her.

As he got out, so did she. He secured the car, said, 'Lead the way,' and walked by her side up the drive to the house.

Suzanne appeared first at the living-room door. Her father was working at the bureau in the corner. He looked over his shoulder. 'Miles with you?' he asked. Suzanne shook her head. 'I thought I heard someone come in with you. Where's your mother?'

'Next door with Mrs Hardy.'

'I thought as much. Give her a call and tell her to come home.'

Suzanne ignored her father's imperious demand. Ross walked into the room, hands in his slacks pockets. He had removed his jacket and he stood, head high, the length and breadth of him intimidating yet exciting her at the same time.

Lucas glanced over his shoulder again, hearing the movement. He did a double-take and flung down his pen, swinging his ample body round and getting to his feet. He approached Ross, who stood in the centre of the room.

Lucas put his hands on his hips and thrust his head forward. 'Right, you've made your presence known. You can turn right round,' he made a circling movement with his finger, 'and go straight out again. What's more, if you don't go willingly,' his complexion was reddening, 'I'll put you out with my own hands.'

Ross did not move. He gazed steadily down at the flaming face of the man gazing up at him.

'Did you hear what I said?'

'I'm staying, Mr Cannon,' Ross answered quietly.

Lucas's fist came out and struck his opponent's arm, the solid muscle of it warding off the blow like a ball bouncing off a stone wall. Suzanne knew that action, had felt it in the past many times. She had not flinched, either, not once, although it had caused her pain both in her arm and her heart.

Ross's jaw moved, his eyes flickered, but he stayed exactly where he was. Suzanne knew the blow would be followed by another, and she stepped in front of Ross, protecting him, but two hands from behind her gripped her waist and flung her aside. Suzanne regained her balance with difficulty.

'There's no need for self-sacrifice,' Ross's voice grazed. 'I can look after myself, and deal with a mulish father-in-law.'

Lucas staggered back to his chair, carrying on the fight with his eyes. 'I'll never acknowledge you as my son-in-law, never,' he said, with hate in his voice.

Ross responded as though he had never spoken. 'I've come to talk business, not for social reasons, nor to seek a reconciliation.'

'Business? What the devil do you know about my business?'

'Only what your daughter told me.'

'Your daughter', Suzanne thought, not 'my wife'.

Lucas swivelled towards her. 'What damned right have you got telling *him* about my business?' He went over to her, making a threatening gesture. 'Have you been blabbing about my——'

Ross took a stride to stand beside her, putting his arm across her shoulders. It was a clear warning—touch her and you'll be sorry.

Lucas looked from one to the other. His ample figure seemed to slump into itself. He walked back slowly to his chair. He sat forward, elbows on his knees, hands rubbing over his forehead.

'She's going to marry Bill Harringdon's boy,' he muttered, half to himself, then banged fist against palm. 'She's got to marry Miles!'

Recovering himself, he straightened. 'Well, miss, what did you tell him?' A pointing finger avoided the use of his son-in-law's name.

'Very little,' Ross answered for her, 'except to indicate that you had cash-flow problems.'

'I don't like your fancy language,' Lucas blustered. 'I need money, not cash-flow. My business isn't quite down the drain, but it's looking for a gutter to flow along. There, now it's all out in the open. And,' with almost bared teeth, 'all in the family. So,' with a sneering glance at Ross, 'what do you intend to do about it? Disown the girl because her father's company's grinding to a halt, so she won't have any money to inherit?'

Ross walked slowly towards Lucas. 'I said I came to talk business, not to listen to a stream of insults.' He thrust hands into his pockets, emphasising the breadth of his hips. 'Let's talk in plain language. How much money do you need?'

Lucas stood up again. 'I'm darned if I'm going to tell you!'

'I'll start again. How much money do you want?'

Piercing blue eyes met angry grey. 'Why the devil should I——? He sank into his chair. 'A hell of a lot.'

Suzanne's heart lifted a just a little. Her father had stopped blustering. He was giving Ross a chance.

'What about your bank?'

'Not a cent more will they give me. Had it straight from the top man himself.'

'I might have access to a sum of money. Exactly how much do you need?'

Lucas told him, and Suzanne put a hand to her head. But Ross did not react. They're talking, she thought, closing her eyes momentarily, like—no, not like friends, like—father to son! I can't believe it, she thought, I just can't believe it.

'My credit rating is good,' Ross said thoughtfully.

Lucas's head came up. 'How good?'

'Good enough.'

Lucas frowned. 'Where have you been all these years? Robbing banks?'

A joke? Suzanne thought wonderingly. Her father had made a joke—with Ross? But this was business, something her father thrived on. It did not mean he had accepted Ross as a person, nor as a son-in-law.

'Not exactly.' Ross's smile had faded quickly. 'I'm a geologist. I work for an oil company.' He gave the name of an internationally-known consortium.

'Oil, eh? There's a fair amount of money in that.'

'Enough. I've saved. Not much you can spend it on where I've been.'

'You're on leave, and you're going back?' There was

a trace of hope in the question.

Ross shook his head. 'I've been promoted. Office job in London, at U.K. headquarters. Higher position, more money.'

Lucas's eyes darkened. 'My daughter's divorcing you. She's marrying Bill Harringdon's boy.'

Ross's eyes became a deeper blue. 'Let's talk business, shall we? Tomorrow I'll start things going.'

'Know your bank manager well, eh? On social terms with him?'

'I never act the sycophant, Mr Cannon. I told you, my credit rating's good. I'll raise the money you want. It should get you out of your short-term troubles, help your company back on its feet. When it's steady again, you can start repaying me.'

'And what interest would you be thinking of asking, then? Double what the bank demands from you?'

There was a sound from the doorway, and Lucas's attention was distracted from the discussion. 'Cynthia! It's about time. Where the devil have you been?'

His wife was not listening. Her eyes were opened wide, she was staring at the stranger. 'Ross?' she asked in a whisper.

Ross turned to greet her, approaching and holding out his hand. 'Mrs Cannon.' His other hand covered hers.

Suzanne watched Ross's expression soften. 'It's good to meet you again.'

Cynthia continued to look wonderingly up at the young man. 'You've changed,' she murmured, unable to keep the admiration from her eyes.

'We all get older, Mrs Cannon.'

Once, Suzanne thought, he looked at me in that gentle way.

'That's enough,' Lucas said sharply, glowering at the expression on his wife's face. 'We were talking business. Sit down, Cynthia, if you're going to stay.'

Cynthia looked questioningly at her husband, then their visitor, apparently unable to come to a decision. Ross made it for her, leading her to a chair. She thanked him with an uncertain smile.

'Don't try insinuating yourself into the good books of your mother-in-law,' Lucas snarled.

Ross turned quickly, anger glittering in his eyes. 'Since I'm the one offering my help to you in your troubles, I think I'm entitled to behave how I damned well please, don't you? Especially where my mother-in-law's concerned.'

He was playing Lucas at his own game—using nastiness as a weapon to demonstrate superior power. It worked, as Ross seemed to know it would.

Lucas took a hold on his temper, thrust forward his fleshy jaw, swung to shuffle through papers on the bureau, then swung back. 'I was asking you about interest.' He had managed to shift his tone to neutral.

'Until your company gets on its feet again,' Ross stated, 'I shall pay the interest.'

Lucas stared. 'You'll what?'

'You heard me, Mr Cannon. When the business starts to recover, you will take over the interest payments.'

Cynthia urged forward in her chair. 'But that might take some while, mightn't it, Lucas?' To Ross, she said before her husband could intervene, 'That will prove an awful burden on your back, Ross, won't it?'

Ross's shoulders lifted and fell. His glance swivelled to rest on his wife's tense figure. 'If it does, I'll be doing it for the sake of the family to which I'm joined by marriage.'

'Oh, Ross,' Cynthia said with deep sincerity, 'I think you're being wonderfully generous.'

'Suzanne's divorcing him,' Lucas snapped. 'She's marrying Miles as soon as she's free. Then,' with a resentful glare at Ross, 'I can pay off his loan. As soon as Bill Harringdon can give me one to take its place, that is. I'll be able to say that,' he made a thrusting, on-your-way gesture in Ross's direction, 'to *his* loan.'

'Not so fast, Mr Cannon,' Ross declared with a curl to his lips. 'You haven't got my loan yet. You see, I'm going to make a condition.'

'Condition? I damned well won't accept any condition you've got the cheek to impose!'

Ross strolled towards the older man, ignoring his blustering attitude.

'And that condition is,' Ross declared, 'that for the duration of the loan, or until the divorce is through, whichever is the first, I want my wife to come back and live with me.'

Suzanne paled, walking towards him. 'Live with you where?'

'I've bought a house, had it furnished. It's large. There's plenty of room for both of us.'

'She can't live with you!' Lucas almost shouted. 'She's filing a petition for a divorce.'

'We shall live our separate lives. I told you when I came back a few weeks ago that I wanted her back.'

'You'd move mountains, you said,' Suzanne put in. She faced him squarely, eyes flashing. 'You know what you are? An unscrupulous——'

'Did I forget to mention,' he cut in smoothly, 'that the divorce will not go undefended?'

'It makes no difference,' she claimed. 'We've been apart for so long, I'll still get the divorce.'

'I know that. I just intend to prolong the whole procedure.'

'I suppose I don't have any say in the matter?' Suzanne commented acidly.

'None at all,' Ross dismissed, and turned back to Lucas. 'Well, Mr Cannon, do you accept the terms?'

'She's going to marry Miles, I tell you,' he answered.

'But Lucas,' Cynthia spoke from behind them, 'if Ross can lend you the money and if Suzanne doesn't mind going back to Ross ... I mean,' her voice was tailing off in the face of her husband's contorted features, 'she is his wife.'

Lucas was breathing hard, unable to express the fury he was feeling. In the face of his son-in-law's reasonableness, his offer and his generosity in accepting the liability of paying the interest, he was powerless. Pride prevented him from relinquishing the power he had, until now, been able to wield in order to utilise people to his own ends.

Ross shrugged carelessly. 'I've done my best to help. Forget the whole idea. Goodbye, Mr Cannon, Mrs Cannon.' He was at the door.

Suzanne felt a cry rise into her throat. If she let him walk out of her life again, she knew it would be final. She could not discover exactly what she felt for him. Six years of separation was such a long time and she had been so young when she had thought she loved him enough to marry him. One thing she did know—she did not, at that moment, want to let him go.

'I'll do as you want. I'll live with you, in your house, separately. Then my father can have the money he needs.'

Lucas seemed to deflate like a punctured balloon. He held his head, resting on the desk.

'Such sacrifice for the sake of your father's company,' Ross said with deep sarcasm.

She held his gaze, her white face and stiff determination disguising her fear of what the future might hold. There was no doubt in her mind that she had adored the man she had married, but that was a long time ago. Now, a stranger calling himself her husband was demanding that in exchange for helping her father she must go back and live with him as his wife-in-name.

'It won't stop me filing a petition for divorce,' she declared defiantly.

His eyes did not flicker, nor leave her face. What kind of a man had he grown into in their years apart that he could stand there as emotionally immovable as a carved figure? Something inside her was challenged by his unreadable mask of a face. Was there nothing about her that touched him any more?

A week later, the telephone rang. Since Suzanne was alone in the house, she answered.

'Ross here,' the voice said briskly, making no concession to the fact that he was speaking to his wife.

In spite of herself, Suzanne's heart beat faster. It was coming nearer, she told herself, that moment when she would have to go and live with him.

'I've negotiated the loan for your father,' he told her. 'I've written to him setting out the terms of the agreement. It contains that condition to which you agreed. When he signs and returns it, and I arrive to collect you, I shall hand over the cheque.' Suzanne could not bring herself to answer.

'Did you hear me?' Ross demanded.

'I heard you. I just don't like your unethical way of doing business. Nor do I like the idea of being treated as just a clause in a contract.'

'That's too bad,' he returned curtly, 'it's something you'll have to accept.'

Suzanne swallowed down her retort. What use was it opposing him? 'When will the exchange of "clause" and cheque take place?'

'Two days from now. Can you make it?'

'How considerate of you to ask me,' she answered acidly. 'The "clause" will be free to walk out at your side in two days. It's not easy to argue with a blackmailer.'

'Okay, so I'm a blackmailer. It makes no difference what you think of me.'

'I'll tell my father the good news. He still hasn't forgiven me for marrying you seven years ago. Every hour of every day that he's been home this week, he hasn't let me forget it.'

'And I,' the voice said, dangerously softly, 'haven't forgiven you for leaving me six years ago. Nor will *I* let you forget it.'

Suzanne slammed down the phone and breathed deeply to regain control. She would have to let Miles know that she would be moving. For a moment, she racked her brains as to how to explain a move on her part which might appear to him to be somewhat quixotic in all the circumstances.

Miles himself answered when she rang his father's

number. In the past week of waiting, she had not seen him, having refused his invitation to a meal on the grounds of being too busy finishing certain items for sale in the shop.

It was plain that he was growing impatient to see her again. 'Can you make it tonight?' he asked.

'Sorry, Miles, too busy again. But not for the same reasons. I—I thought I'd better explain. It—well, it might come as a bit of a shock to you, but Ross has asked me to go and live with him again.'

'You mean there's been a reconciliation?' Miles asked, the dismay in his tone almost painful to hear.

'Not that, Miles. It was just——' she sought desperately for inspiration, 'that with his new position—it's at the head office of the oil company he works for—he's moved up the career ladder quite a few rungs. He explained how he needed to have his——' she swallowed, 'his wife living under his roof, and acting as hostess whenever necessary. I didn't want to be accused of having jeopardised his career, and it is only until the divorce, so I agreed,' she finished lamely, mentally mopping her brow.

'So it's the end of our engagement?'

Gently, she explained, 'We weren't really engaged, were we, Miles? I mean, the engagement only becomes real when the divorce is through. I should have told you that Ross said we would live our separate lives.'

'So I haven't got to stop seeing you?'

'Of course not.' The 'separate lives' part applied to her, she thought with some defiance, as well as to Ross. 'Just as long as we're discreet about it.'

'I'll be discreet all right,' he answered in a voice which told her that it had just occurred to him that going out with a married woman added a little more spice to their relationship. 'Otherwise,' he went on, 'it would cancel out the whole reason for your going to live with him.'

'Quite right,' she said, thinking that, appearances apart, in coping with the man her husband had changed into, discretion would be an essential part of such an extra-marital relationship, no matter how innocent it was in essence.

'When will you be going?' Miles asked, and when told, exclaimed, 'That soon?'

'I knew about it a week ago. He gave me time to think it over. I didn't want to tell you anything definite until I was sure I could go through with it.'

Miles appeared to accept the explanation and asked for her new address.

When the letter enclosing the agreement arrived, Suzanne's father was at first angry, muting this to a burning resentment as he signed it. How he really felt about being helped out of his difficulties by the son-in-law he did not wish to accept, Suzanne did not know, since as usual he hid his real feelings under a cloak of blustering abuse. Using his daughter as a bargaining weapon did not seem to stir his conscience in any way.

On the afternoon of the appointed day, Suzanne carried her suitcases downstairs and went to find her mother. At the touch of her daughter's arm round her shoulders, Cynthia started crying.

Soothing her as well as she could, Suzanne wondered if, in her imagination, her mother was acting out the maternal parent's role at the departure of her daughter into the care and keeping of her new husband—a role she had been denied at the time the marriage took place.

Suzanne had not yet seen her new home, but Ross had told her it was only a few miles away. 'I won't be going far, Mum,' Suzanne said reassuringly, 'and there's always the telephone. Anyway, it won't be for ever, will it? It's only a temporary arrangement, we know that.'

Cynthia nodded, drying her eyes. Her husband entered and saw the action. Immediately, he grumbled, 'What the blazes are you crying for? She's going where she belongs, to live in the house of the man she,' he indicated his daughter with some distaste, 'in her un-worldly wisdom, got herself married to, when she should have listened to her parents, who'd said "no".' He looked at the papers he held. 'In the event, I can't really grumble. He's proved useful in tiding the company over until she marries Miles and Bill Harringdon lends me the money I need.'

'There's only the matter of a divorce in the way, isn't there, Father?' Suzanne asked ironically.

'And that cold-hearted swine of a husband of yours has promised to make things difficult,' Lucas cursed. 'Not that he can prevent the divorce from going through, not after so many years apart.'

Cold-hearted, her father had called him. So even he had noticed, Suzanne thought. That was part of the character-change Ross had undergone since she had married him. He had been strong-minded in those days, but not—most certainly not—cold. The passion they had shared in those stolen days together had burned them both with its strength.

As the doorbell rang, Suzanne felt the vibrations shake her tense body. Her parents looked at her, waiting. It was the end of something, she felt, but although she groped with her mind, she could not find a clue. Maybe it was a beginning, too?

He stood, unsmiling, on the doorstep. His shirt was a deep blue, his well-fitting cords even darker. A fawn-coloured jacket was slung over his shoulder. Spoiling the image of weekend-man relaxing was an executive case in his left hand. His body gave a take-it-easy message, his expression said 'business'.

His blue eyes skimmed her sleeveless blue dress, her shoulder-length red-brown hair. Her wide, apprehensive gaze and the slightly-parted lips seemed also not to have escaped his notice. He gave no hint of the nature of his thoughts.

His half-smile lacked amusement as he said, 'You haven't come to meet your doom. May I come in?'

Suzanne regained her poise at once, opening the door wider. He glanced at the cases. 'Is that all?' he asked. 'You seem to be underestimating the time you'll be with me. It takes longer than you think to tear apart a legal relationship, especially when it's defended. Where is your father?'

Finding herself unable to speak, she nodded towards the living-room. She followed Ross, standing beside him as he regarded his father-in-law's back.

'Mr Cannon?' Ross said.

Lucas continued to bend over the antique desk, writing.

It's the old trick, Suzanne fumed, keeping a caller waiting, thus hoping to reduce him in stature. Ross, who was starting to open his case, refastened it.

'Right,' he stated, 'I'll tear up the cheque and go.'

Lucas swung round, red in the face. 'You upstart! How dare you talk to me——!' His wife was silencing him frantically with a flapping hand. Lucas swallowed his abuse together with his pride, and rose.

Ross waited until his father-in-law's breathing had returned to normal. 'I've come,' he said, 'to hand over the loan I'm making you and take delivery of the surety.'

'Surety? Clause? Condition? What else are you going to call me?' Suzanne demanded, her colour rising.

'Surety?' her father echoed with even more anger. 'Are you doubting my word, you young whipper-snapper, that I'll repay you this loan?' He held up the cheque which Ross had given him.

Ross's hand was gripping Suzanne's arm now. Try as she might, she could not dislodge it.

'It's not your word I'm doubting, Mr Cannon. You have to prove you can use that money to get your company on its feet. Only then will you be able to repay me.' He glanced round at his captive. 'Only when every single penny of that money has been given back to me by you will I let Suzanne go.'

'When the divorce is over you'll have to.' Ross stayed silent. 'Do you hear?' Lucas shouted, his cheeks dyed scarlet.

Ross chose not to answer the question. Instead, he persisted, 'I suggest that if you want your friend

Harringdon to give you financial help, you'd do well to get your business on a firm footing. In which case, you won't be able to repay the loan until he's forthcoming with his donation.'

'But I can't ask for his help until she's married to his son, or at the very least, engaged to the man.'

'That, Mr Cannon, is your problem.'

'I repeat,' Suzanne said through her teeth, 'you're unscrupulous.'

'Aren't you glad,' Ross asked her sarcastically, 'that I'm proving you right in your accusation? You've learnt to read character well, my love, since you married me and then left me six years ago. You're so right—I am unscrupulous.'

'Lucas,' Cynthia said, standing up, 'I think you should thank Ross instead of being so unpleasant to him.' Her husband merely studied the writing on the cheque. 'He's been so good to us in lending you that money.'

'I'm waiting until this cheque clears before I thank him,' Lucas growled.

Cynthia let out a short, exasperated breath. 'Well, since my husband is being so ungracious, Ross, I'll thank you instead.' She held out her hand. He took it with a smile and she looked up into his eyes. 'Suzanne's special, Ross,' she said softly. 'Treat her well, won't you?' She drew him down to kiss his cheek as Lucas stamped out of the room.

When it was Suzanne's turn, she put her arms around her mother's shoulders. ''Bye, Mum. See you soon. I'll ring you. Take care.'

Her father was not even there to see her go.

Suzanne forced back the moisture that had invaded her eyes and gazed boldly up at the man at her side. 'I'm ready,' she told him.

The house was built on a ridge which it shared with two others, all three being spaced to give a more than ample area between each building for complete privacy.

Trees formed another screen from neighbours. The

house had been added to over the years, so that much of it was modern. The older part, Suzanne judged, was probably built at the turn of the century.

Its view from the front lay across the fields and was magnificent. Suzanne felt at one with the place immediately. 'How long have you owned it?' she asked, as Ross led the way into the lobby carrying two of her cases while she carried the other.

'About four weeks. It was standing empty. I had it redecorated and furnished.'

Which explained, Suzanne estimated, why she had heard nothing from him for those strangely empty weeks. 'Is all this——' she included the living-area in the sweep of her arm, 'your taste?'

'Not entirely.' Suzanne looked at him, hoping he would elaborate, but he declined to do so.

'So the decorators advised you?' she prompted, but he was walking towards the dining recess which occupied an alcove.

Disturbed by the unanswered questions, she looked at the boldly patterned brown and white carpet, at the heavy velvet curtains, at the cream-coloured four-seater couch and deep chairs to match. There was no need for him to tell her anything, she tried to reason, since she was only a temporary addition, a kind of non-paying guest. All the same, she could not rid herself of a feeling of disquietude.

The entire outer wall of the dining-alcove was made of glass. His back was to her as he gazed out at an area of green which must surely be the garden. His fingers were spread over his hips, his elbows bent, his broad back straight.

He turned and walked towards her slowly. The sight of him made her heart turn over. He had changed not only character-wise, she told herself yet again, but in his build. Toughness of mind vied with the muscle-power of his limbs to establish superiority. Neither had won, for each was equal to the other.

'Please sit down,' he invited. 'Would you like a drink?'

She shook her head, feeling at the same time the chill breeze of his politeness brush over her skin. He bent down and lifted her hand. 'While you're living with me, I'd be glad if you would dispose of that engagement ring and wear the wedding ring I gave you. That is, if you've still got it.'

Raking in her bag, she extracted an envelope, tipping the wedding ring on to her palm. He picked it up, examining it while she slipped Miles' ring into the envelope and pushed it into her bag.

He was reading the inscription engraved on the inside of the band. 'Suzanne. For ever my love. Ross', it said. He lifted her hand again, saying mockingly, 'With this ring I thee re-wed.' He pushed the ring into place and she looked at it, not wanting to meet his eyes.

After a while she looked up at him, only to find him studying her. 'I'll give Miles his ring back,' she offered, to break the strained silence.

'That's up to you,' he dismissed. 'Now, where would you like to eat this evening, here or at a restaurant?' His tone was so neutral she wanted to say something outrageous to unbalance him. He was so much in command of himself, she knew that would be impossible.

'Is there food in the house?' she asked at last.

'Plenty. Can you cook?' It seemed ridiculous that, as her husband, he should be asking her.

'To a certain standard, no better, no worse.' She rose and found herself facing him. Unsure in the face of his complete self-confidence, she moved quickly, putting a distance between them. 'If you'll show me where the kitchen is——?'

He led her into the dining alcove, through a communicating door and into the kitchen. 'It's a dream!' Suzanne exclaimed. 'Was it like this when you bought the place, or have you had it redesigned?'

'I asked experts for their advice and then let them get on with it. I'm glad you like the result.' His tone was neutral.

It annoyed her because she wanted him to share her

pleasure. Then she reminded herself again that her stay there was temporary. 'Of course,' she heard her own voice say, 'I'm just a "clause" with two legs, part of a deal. When you've finished with me, when the loan's been repaid to you, you'll throw me out with the garbage.' Her shoulders lifted exaggeratedly, her back to him. 'Why should I care? I've got Miles to run to.'

Her shoulders were seized and she was turned forcefully. She found herself looking up at a face whose features were hauntingly familiar, yet which distressed her by their chilling dissimilarity from those she had once known and loved.

'What did you tell Harringdon?' His grip was bruisingly tight. 'What explanation did you give him for moving in here?'

'That—that you'd moved up the career ladder and needed your wife living under your roof for—for appearances' sake and to be your hostess.'

'Nothing else? Not a word about the loan?'

'Nothing else, I swear.'

His grip eased, but he did not release her. If all her deep-seated fear of him and all her bewilderment about his character-change was in her eyes, she neither knew nor cared. At that moment, as her gaze tried in vain to read his thoughts and he as resolutely shut her out of them, there was only one thing she wanted.

Had he read that in her eyes? Maybe he had, since his head lowered and his lips brushed her mouth. Lifting away, she was able to see that the contact, far from pleasing, had angered him. His jaw ridged. 'I don't *know* you. I want to learn again the feel of you, your body against mine.' He jerked her to him. 'I'm your husband. Why the hell shouldn't I?'

His hands were all over her, pressing her waist, sliding to her hips, skimming her thighs, moulding upwards to the softness of her breasts. Suzanne's breath caught in her throat. He was rekindling fires long burnt to ashes, or so she had told herself many times across the years.

'You can't claim any rights,' she cried, 'even though

we're married. It was all so long ago, it's meaningless now.' She struggled free, smoothing her dress. 'You can't treat me like a plaything, picking me up and fondling me whenever the fancy takes you, then throwing me down and walking away. Not any more.'

'Did I ever have to "pick you up"? I seem to remember there was a time that you flung yourself at me and wouldn't let me rest until I'd loved you and loved you again.'

His taunting words brought a tremble to her lips. 'I was a terrible wife in those days, wasn't I?' Her voice was thickening. 'I wanted your love in exchange for mine. That was a terrible crime, wasn't it?'

Ross's lips disappeared in a thin line. He threw her from him, strode out of the room and went quickly up the stairs. A few moments later, he reappeared in the kitchen. 'I've taken your cases up to your room. It's the third on the left, next to mine. The bathroom is opposite your bedroom.'

'Thanks, Ross. I——' she wanted to make amends before all chance of establishing even friendship between them slipped away, 'I shouldn't have said what I did. You've been good to my father. I should have thanked you for that.'

'Let me assure you, I did not do what I did for him. As you're so fond of saying, I did it for your mother's sake. I can see she leads a hell of a life with him. All the same,' he paused as he moved away, 'despite her slender build, my observations tell me that she's able to stand on her own two feet. He's not as invulnerable as he likes to appear to her gentle manner.' His faintly contemptuous glance flicked over her. 'You could do with some of your mother's gentleness. It would improve you beyond words.'

'Too bad for you, then,' with determination she kept her voice steady, 'that I take so much after my father!'

He advanced towards her, head slightly lowered. 'Oh, do you? Thanks for the information. I shall take the greatest pleasure in knocking it out of you.'

'I'm divorcing you,' she replied, the pitch of her voice rising. 'In a few months I won't be here for you to "knock anything out of me".'

'So I must make the most of the time I've got, mustn't I?' The look in his blue eyes pierced her to her depths. Then I can hand you over to your true love meek and mild enough to eat out of his hand.'

Suzanne wanted to cry. Instead, she hit back, 'I'll never be meek and mild!'

'No? We'll see. But not tonight. I'm going out to eat.'

'What about me?' The question from her own lips took her unawares.

'We're living separate lives, remember? I'm going to find myself a more amenable dinner partner.'

He left the house, the door slamming behind him.

# CHAPTER FIVE

SUZANNE awoke to a bright day, but she felt no echoing brightness inside her. For a long time she had not slept, lying in the wide bed which had been made up for her, listening for Ross's return. When she woke in the small hours, she wondered if he had returned at all. Or had she missed him when sleep had finally come?

The evening had been a long one. Finding food in the fridge, she had made herself a scratch meal. Having worked out how to operate the television set, she found the programmes had been unable to hold her attention. Even then, she had been listening for Ross.

Flinging the covers aside, she found her towelling mules, pulled on a dressing-gown and made her way across to the bathroom. When she had first seen it the night before, she had gasped at its opulence.

It was a large room and carpeted. Lighting glowed from an illuminated ceiling. The bath was sunken, with chrome handles and corner taps. Wandering round, Suzanne felt that Ross's presence seemed to linger despite his absence. It seemed he had risen earlier, since his personal belongings lay scattered over glass shelves and vanity units, of which there were two.

Bending down, she adjusted the plug and turned on the taps, for a moment watching the steam rise. There were thick, large towels on the heated rails, perfumed salts in jars, talc and a collection of bottles.

Who had been thoughtful enough to put them there? For whom were they intended? Did Ross remember her choice in such matters? Or—and the idea brought her thoughts to a crashing stop—did they all belong to some other woman?

Wandering round simply for the pleasure of it, she found damp footsteps leading away from the glass-fronted shower cubicle. She fitted her own feet into them, smiling. It seemed that Ross had showered after shaving. Remembering the water, she dashed to the bath's side and turned off the taps, then, scattering rose-scented bath salts into the water, she lowered herself into it.

Twenty minutes later she climbed out and wrapped herself in the thick folds of a large white towel. Rubbing herself dry, she searched among the bottles and found a pink-shaded liquid called 'after-bath lotion'. Dropping the towel, she rubbed it down her arms and over her body, when something made her pause and look into the large mirror along one wall.

Behind her, a man stood watching. Her heart leapt, first with fright, then with apprehension. His arms were folded and he was leaning on his shoulder against the closed door. She swung to face him, eyes opened wide, lips parted. 'What are you doing in here?' she asked angrily, telling herself her heated cheeks were the result of a hot bath. If he touched her, she panicked, what would she do?

As she felt his cool eyes creep all over her, embarrassment made her conscious of just how much of her she was allowing him to see. Turning back to the mirror, she met his eyes and the small smile of derision which played about his lips. The reflection appeared to be as intriguing to him as the reality.

'Get out of here!' she ordered, but a treacherous weakness in her limbs deprived the words of power. She folded her arms across her. How could she speak imperiously when the very sight of him, especially there and in such circumstances, made her knees feel as soft as lamb's wool?

Ross lifted himself upright and moved round the sunken bath. She reached for the towel, but he knocked it out of her hand. 'Why try to hide from me, your husband?' His eyes, reflected by the mirror, although cool in essence, made her burn as they mocked yet admired. He was not touching her, yet she experienced the imagined feel of his hands as potently as the real, remembered thing.

'Please,' she pleaded, 'leave me alone.' At once she cursed herself for giving away to him her vulnerability.

He was not slow to decode the scrambled message. He moved nearer so that his clothed body touched her cooling, scented skin. A shiver of alarm coursed through her as deep-frozen memories began to melt.

'So the magic hasn't entirely gone?' he commented, eyelids drooping as if he knew exactly how she was feeling. His head bent and his lips rested in the hollow of her throat. He inhaled deeply and asked, his mouth moving caressingly against her, 'Why the perfume? Have you decided to remain married to me after all?'

He was overpowering her with his presence, his half-kiss, his negative lovemaking. Turning swiftly, she declared, 'Even if I had no other reason for divorcing you, I'd still do it. *You* aren't the man I married.' She took a breath before she uttered the coming untruth, 'I could never fall in love with you now, if we'd never met before.'

The glint in his eyes frightened her. Her defences were nil. Every weapon was on his side. He seized her upper arms and swung her to the carpeted floor, and a few seconds later his heavier form was imprisoning hers. The feel of his clothed body on her uncovered skin was both frustrating and immensely potent. Her arms found their way round his neck and she stared, eyes bright with expectation, at his hard-angled face, waiting for his kiss.

It did not come. Instead, he tugged her arms away and rolled on to his side, looking her recumbent body over, eyes making love where she longed for his touch to feed the fire.

'So eager,' he remarked caustically. 'Are you like this with all your lovers? If you are, no wonder Miles Harringdon can't wait for you to split from me and marry him!'

He stood up, glancing with blue-slitted eyes at her tremulous, unkissed lips, her taut, disappointed shapeli-

ness, her tensed limbs. She started to shiver with in-
creasing chill under the impact of his cold gaze.

He turned for the towel, dropped it on to her and
went to the door. 'It was an interesting encounter. It's
answered a few questions.'

Suzanne scrambled to her feet, eyes stormy as she
stared back, pulling the towel around her. If he dared to
accuse her again of flinging herself at him . . .

Ross tossed a last remark through the opened door.
'You've improved with keeping, which is something that
couldn't be said of some women I've known.'

Bending, she seized the sponge and threw it at him. It hit
the closed door futilely as the sound of his laughter faded.


Looking around in the kitchen, Suzanne noted the used
place at the breakfast counter. So Ross had eaten. From
the look of his plate, he had cooked himself an egg.

It was strange to think of Ross being able to cook,
although she told herself she shouldn't be surprised after
their year—or parts of it—together in the shared house
where he had lived as a student. He had cooked then,
for them both.

It seemed he had forgotten those days. Either that or
her existence, since there was no sign of any cooked
food for her. Well, she lifted her shoulders under the
sleeveless blue dress she had chosen to wear, she too
could cook. Making toast, poaching an egg, she felt her
appetite increase. He had left the marmalade for her,
not in a pot but a jar. Yes, that figured, she reasoned. A
left-over habit from the old days? Or roughing it in the
jungle of Nigeria?

Coffee was next, she thought, looking around without
success to discover if there was a percolator functioning.
Maybe Ross had not had any, and if so . . . Her feet
took her through the dining alcove and into the living-
room with its air of waiting to be occupied. Past the
dining-area were two glass-paned doors, wide open to
allow the morning sunlight to flood the place to the
very corners.

Ross was seated in an upright garden chair. His back was to the house and he appeared to be absorbed in paperwork. His shirt was dark blue and short-sleeved, his slacks, pulled taut around his thighs by his crossed legs, were dark and casual. His strong profile, the leanness of his body tugged at her heartstrings.

Tearing her eyes away, she glanced at the well-kept garden, following the deep green of the lawn as it sloped steeply downwards to widen towards the end, giving a glimpse of rectangular blue. Ross had not told her there was a swimming pool.

'Did you want me?' His indifferent voice told her he had noticed her.

'Only to ask if you'd like some coffee.'

'I had some with my breakfast, thanks. Er——' he called her back, 'you don't object to the instant variety, I hope? Where I've lived, ground coffee and percolators were looked on as belonging to the so-called civilised sections of society.'

'And you were strictly uncivilised.'

'Purely primitive. Positively primeval.'

Suzanne laughed at his turn of phrase.

He grinned. 'I recommend it as a way of life. You must try it some time.'

Her smile held, but she was thinking, With you, only with you. Reluctantly she turned and went away. It was good, laughing with him again. It was the laughter she had missed most for those long years. After the divorce, she would miss it for the rest of her life.

Having drunk her coffee, Suzanne returned to her room to tidy the bed. That done, she looked along the corridor to the patterned glass door which, she calculated, led to the modern addition she had noticed when they had arrived.

A quick glance over her shoulder told her that the door of Ross's bedroom was shut. With light footsteps, she hurried over the carpeted floor and made her way through to the unexplored regions.

There seemed to be a self-contained apartment, together with bathroom and kitchen. Beyond that was a furnished office and more bedrooms, plus another bath-room. Suzanne was puzzled as to why, in the circum-stances, Ross had chosen to buy such a large house. It was a question she dared not ask him.

Returning, she went down the stairs to discover that he was where she had left him. To her surprise, another chair had been placed on the patio within talking—but not touching—distance. Without asking permission, she sat in the chair, her eyes captured by the view from the rear of the house. Fields stretched into the distance, green and growing. It was plainly part of a farm whose produce was agricultural.

Filling her lungs with the fresh-smelling air, she leaned her head back and closed her eyes. She became aware of the fact that something had gone from her. Despite her virtual captivity, it was a curious feeling of freedom. There was tension, but of a kind that excited.

It was then that she realised what that missing 'something' was. Again, it was tension, but of a bad kind, such as that generated by the ill-feeling which emanated from her father. That was the freedom she was experiencing. There were no harsh words, no raging and unfounded accusations to counter, no mother to protect—and who could protect herself, anyway.

'Suzanne?' Ross's enunciation of her name gave her a pleasant shock. Only he spoke it in that special way. She turned her head. 'You seem—content. Are you?'

A deep sigh came from her. 'Maybe.' He did not press for an explanation, but she told him, 'It's so peaceful without my father's constant haranguing. It was like fighting a war all the time.'

He stared grimly at the papers fastened on the clip-board on his lap.

'Ross? Exactly why did you make my father that loan? Don't tell me it was out of loyalty to your father-in-law, because I know you'd be lying.'

His smile was tight and he shifted his chair a little more in her direction. 'How many times do you need telling? To get you back as I swore I would.'

'But you haven't got me back—not permanently. Only until the divorce. Anyway,' she ventured, 'why did you want me back?'

'You told Harringdon the reason. For appearances' sake, wasn't it, to get myself a hostess to go with my new and exalted position in life?'

His sarcasm silenced her and she returned to watching the view. A few moments later, she asked, 'Why are there feminine things in the bathroom, like talc and lotions? Did you buy them for me?' Her smile told him she did not really believe that he had.

Two or three seconds on, her smile faded. 'I have a woman friend, Tania Marlowe. She was with me in Africa.'

'As your—secretary?' Suzanne's question was asked more in hope than conviction.

'She's a geologist.'

'Like you.'

'Like me.' There was a long pause. 'You asked yesterday who helped me furnish this house. She guided me in my choice of a lot of the things I bought.'

Suzanne nodded, unable to speak because her throat was so tight. Why shouldn't he have a woman friend? she tried to rationalise. *More* than a friend ... A man as virile as he was would need a woman——

'The phone's ringing,' Ross remarked.

Suzanne, immersed in her thoughts, had not heard it. His voice came from the hall. He sounded sharp. Was it her father?

He returned, all friendliness wiped from his face. 'Your devoted boy-friend.'

'Miles?' Suzanne spoke into the receiver. 'You called on my parents? I suppose they gave you this number. Tonight, for a meal?' Before Ross had told her about his woman friend, she would have declined the invitation. Now, she answered, 'Yes, of course. Why not? Do I think it would be all right if you called for me?' Separate lives, Ross had said, which meant he had no grounds for objection. 'Of course it will. It's a few miles away. You know? See you at seven o'clock. 'Bye, Miles.'

When she returned to the patio, Ross's seat was empty. Nor was there any sign of the work he had been doing. Suzanne stood beside her chair and caught a glimpse of a dark head in the pool. It seemed to be a businesslike swim, undertaken for exercise rather than enjoyment.

The Sunday paper lay between the chairs and she selected the magazine supplement. Flicking through it, she heard Ross making his way towards her from the pool, using the three or four steps which climbed the slope. A towel was round his neck, gathered scarf-like. His wet limbs glinted in the sun, the sinewy muscles moving with each stride. Unable to resist the fascination of his deeply-tanned, gleaming body, she watched his progress. A smile was ready to greet him when he stopped beside her.

He did not stop, nor did he return her smile, continuing on his way as if she was not there. He disappeared, going round the side and through the kitchen.

His deliberate neglect of her presence hurt immeasurably. The magazine lay unread on her lap as she looked again for a sight of the carefully nurtured fields, but they could not give the consolation she sought. She told herself that she had known the position when she had returned to live with Ross. Separate lives, he had said, and he certainly meant it.

After a while, he came back to stand and gaze, as she had done, at the view. Determined to ignore him out of revenge for the way he had ignored her, she gave no sign that she was aware of him. To her dismay, she discovered she did not have his ability to cut himself off. Her eyes were eventually drawn to him.

It seemed she need not have worried about giving her feelings away. Ross had not shifted his gaze from the far distance. His mind had been projected there, too, along with his vision. What was he thinking about? she wondered. Where he had spent the past years? The woman he had left behind in that hot, primitive place?

His attention stayed riveted even when he said, 'I was thinking of a pub lunch. Something light, since you'll be eating out tonight, and so will I.'

With whom? she longed to ask, but pressed her lips together. 'Fine,' she answered, thinking, Going anywhere with you would be a pleasure.

The place Ross had chosen was just off the high street of a nearby small town. It was overflowing with people and good-humour. Side by side, Suzanne and Ross studied the handwritten menu.

'Cottage cheese salad,' Suzanne chose, 'and roll and butter.'

'A ploughman's lunch for me,' Ross told the woman behind the bar, who wrote their order on a pad. She informed them that she would bring the food and Ross led Suzanne to a small, circular table hidden away. He returned for the beer he had ordered for himself and the sherry for which Suzanne had asked, then joined her on the upholstered bench seat.

For a while they drank in silence, listening to the bursts of laughter, the shouts of friends across people's heads. Suzanne enquired, wondering if Ross would give her his attention reluctantly, 'Tomorrow, will you go to work?' He nodded after a swallow of beer. 'Do you drive to London?' He nodded again.

He did not seem to mind her questions, which lightened her heart a little. 'I haven't asked you yet if you can drive,' he remarked.

'Yes, I can drive.'

Their eyes met, and if hers looked empty, then so did his. Perhaps the strangeness had touched him, as it had her, of their lack of knowledge of each others' abilities and achievements, despite their seven-years-long marriage, with its six unfulfilled years apart.

'There's a car for you in the garage, next to mine. It's small but well-made. You'll be able to go and see your mother whenever you like.'

'You bought a car for me?' She was so touched, the words almost caught in her throat.

He nodded. 'And it's not secondhand, if that's what you were thinking.'

There was a tray of food coming in their direction, lifted high over bobbing heads. 'It must have cost you quite a bit,' she commented.

'I'm not exactly poverty-stricken.'

A salad was placed in front of her, a bread roll on a side plate. Suzanne inhaled its fresh aroma. Her eyes were busy sorting green from red and yellow. 'It looks and smells delicious.' She looked up at the woman, smiling. 'A work of art.'

The woman smiled, too, and nodded. 'There's bits of onion in it. I hope your husband doesn't mind.'

'Ah,' Ross reached across and took a sliced white ring, 'thanks for telling me.' As he crunched it, he grinned up at the woman. 'Now when I kiss my wife, she and I won't grumble about each other's breaths, will we, darling?'

Suzanne played up to him. 'I shall enjoy it all the more, darling, knowing you shared something with me.' The woman walked away, laughing.

In the silence she left behind, Suzanne seized her knife and fork and began to eat. Ross took an enormous bite from his chunky, split half-loaf, sandwiched together with a hunk of cheese, pickle and lettuce.

Suzanne laughed at him, she could not stop herself. His jaws looked so puffed out with food. His eyes twinkled as he chewed, then, when he was able to, he grinned back at her. For the second time in a few minutes, they were plunged back into the carefree days of loving and sharing and laughing.

'Did I remember to thank you for the car?' she asked, after a while.

'I don't remember that you did.'

'Well, I do thank you, Ross—very much.'

His dismissing shrug spoilt it all. 'It's useful to have a second car available, also to have a mobile wife.'

'So that she isn't always pestering for a lift?'

He dusted his hands as he finished the last of his lunch. 'That's right.' He wanted an end to the discus-

sion, it was clear from his voice. Well, she would change
the subject. Feeling the pressure of his leg against hers,
she turned to look at him as he sat in a semi-sprawl,
legs stretched under the table, glass half-raised to his
mouth.

He wore a round-necked dark-green jersey with the
points of his shirt-collar lifted out. The cords he had
changed into after his swim moulded themselves around
him. Suzanne had to force down the thrust of feeling
the sight of his careless, faintly abandoned attitude
aroused.

'This morning, Ross, I found the newer part of the
house.' His glass completed its journey to his mouth.
'There are a lot of empty rooms there, aren't there?' He
continued to swallow the mouthfuls. 'What will you do
with them, Ross?'

He stretched forward to place his glass on the table,
then flopped back. 'I'll think of something.'

End of conversation, Suzanne thought, feeling more
put-down than a scolded domestic pet.

Ross straightened, said, 'Excuse me,' and went to the
counter to pay for the food. When he returned, he asked,
'Shall we go, or do you——?' His raised questioning
eyebrows finished the sentence.

'No, thank you. I'll wait until we get home.' She
realised what she had said, flashed an 'I didn't mean it'
look at his ironic smile and went outside with him into
the sunshine.

Ross left her in the living-room reading the news section of the Sunday paper. She heard a door close somewhere in the house. So she was alone. For a while, at
least, she was able to relax. Already she was feeling the
strain of living with the man she loved yet didn't love,
the man she had married having vanished, except for
tantalising glimpses of him.

Losing interest in the article she had been reading,
she folded the paper neatly and put it aside. She had to
do something, she thought. Her feet took her up to her
bedroom. Most of her clothes had been unpacked and

she now emptied the cases, pushing personal items into drawers and putting books on a shelf.

One case was left and this contained the materials for finishing a small presentation basket she was making for sale in Maggie Millet's shop. There was a comfortable bedroom chair in the centre of the room. Sitting on this, she surrounded herself with all the items she would need. Her work-basket was open at her feet.

She was so absorbed in her work that when the knock on the door came, she jumped. Before she could call out in reply, the door was opened and Ross was frowning down at her. If he disapproves, she thought, that's just too bad.

Smiling up at him, she said, 'I'm working. If you object to my working here, I'm sorry, but there was nowhere else. I had to do something. You just went off and left me.'

He came in and closed the door. 'What the hell was I supposed to do—act the nursemaid and never leave you alone? Or perhaps you expected me to play host and entertain you? As for working in here,' he looked around the large room, 'you can do what you damned well like in your bedroom—except entertain your future husband. I draw the line at that.'

Her hands thumped down on to her lap, taking the work with them. 'Don't be stupid, how can I have a "future" husband, when I've got one already? I——'

Realising what she had said made her lips snap shut.

'As you never tire of saying, you're going to divorce me, so it's perfectly possible to have a "future" as well as a "present" husband.'

'I agree,' she answered tautly. 'As usual, your logic never fails. What did you want?'

He looked at the work-basket, at the items strewn round her, at the cane and scissors on her lap. At last, he replied, 'I just wondered where you were.'

He had missed her! In spite of her common sense doing its best to assert itself, her heart skipped. 'Did you think I'd run out on you?'

He leaned back against the door, hands in pockets, head back against the wood. His eyes were hooded as he looked down at her. 'If you had, that would have been the end of your father's loan.'

Her lips tightened. 'You're quite heartless, aren't you?'

'If I were, would I have made the loan in the first place?'

'Yes, to gain your own ends, which were to get me back and force me to live here even if it is only for a few months. You want your revenge, you as good as said so. You'll never forgive me for letting you go off on your own six years ago, nor let me forget it. You said that, too.'

'So what am I doing? Beating you every night?'

Her throat tightened in fear. 'Marital relations are not allowed under the contract. It's part of the conditions of the loan that we live separately.'

Ross walked towards her, in no hurry. 'You've got it wrong. An embargo on that particular activity was certainly not part of any contract I made with your father, only that you come back to me either until the loan was repaid, or until the divorce came through, whichever was the first.'

'I'd better go to the solicitor as soon as I can arrange it, then,' she replied tartly.

'That's up to you. What are you making?' His casual attitude towards her first step on the road to divorcing him incensed her.

'A basket.' She picked up her work. He could not force her to discuss that subject with him. Her work was part of her 'separate life'.

'When I go to work tomorrow, what will you do?'

Suzanne looked up at him in surprise. 'Go to my job, of course.'

'There's no need. I can keep you while you're living with me.'

She put aside her work and stood up, rigid with anger. 'You're certainly not going to "keep" me! I won't allow you to keep a single thing about me. If you buy me clothes, I'll send them back. If you pay for anything, even a meal, I'll pay my share.' She had forgotten how easily she had slipped back into the old habit that lunchtime of allowing him to pay.

He gripped her shoulders, his blue eyes flaring. 'There's plenty about you I shall keep. Memories, for instance—our first days as man and wife, the happiness your beautiful young face radiated after we'd made love, the way you smiled whenever we were together.'

She twisted, trying to free herself.

'And,' he went on relentlessly, 'I shall blank out the lifeless, miserable woman you've become over the years, the woman you are now.' His eyes flicked her upturned, desolate face. 'I'll give you back the insult you handed out to me. If I'd met you now, you would have been the last woman I would have chosen to marry.'

Her lips trembled, but she made them say, 'Get out of my room, get out!'

When he had gone, she stretched across the bed, clutching at the covers, sobbing.

# CHAPTER SIX

THE meal with Miles was made the more tolerable by Ross's presence in the hallway when Miles had arrived.

His contemptuous manner as he witnessed Miles' entrance made Suzanne fling her arms round Miles' neck and lift up her face for a kiss. Miles obliged with alacrity, looking up from the embrace to give Ross a 'she's really mine' message.

Ross's answer had been a cool, unreadable stare beneath which Miles' gaze had dropped. His arm placed possessively round Suzanne, sweeping her to the door, had been his triumphant answer.

They had patronised the same efficiently-run, no-nonsense restaurant. They were greeted by the head waiter and taken to their usual table. The service was as brisk and precise as ever.

Only the conversation was hesitant, with long, unfillable pauses. Over the main course, Miles asked, his eyes on his plate, 'Have you made an appointment with the solicitor to start divorce proceedings?'

Her thoughts had been elsewhere—at the pub where she had sat beside Ross's sprawling form after their simple but satisfying lunch. It was like looking back over the years instead of the hours. As a memory, it had become as precious to her as those of the distant past.

'Sorry.' She was jerked to the present, to the slightly startled and very different face opposite her. How could anyone, a voice cried out from her heart, expect this man ever to take the place of the man who was at that moment her husband? 'Divorce?' she echoed as if it were a word she had never heard before. 'Oh, yes. Yes, I'll have to phone for an appointment.'

'You know it's essential not to delay, don't you?' Miles was saying with urgency. 'I mean, you're living in his house. It's not going to be easy to prove the marriage has broken down, even if you are living separately, if you stay there too long.'

'I know, I know. Don't rush me, Miles, please.' Her hand covered his. 'The situation's—unusual.'

'Yes, it is,' he agreed forcefully, without knowing what she had really meant. 'Exactly why did you go back to him, Suzanne, especially after I'd proposed and you'd accepted?'

'I—I can't tell you, Miles. Not at the moment, anyway.'

His eyes lowered, then lifted. 'It's not because you're——?'

'No, of course it's not. How could I be? Separate lives, remember?'

'I know that, but—but having met him, I wouldn't put it past him to have tried to force himself on you.'

'Well, he hasn't, Miles,' she told him gently. 'Why should he? He wants this divorce as much as I do. He told me this morning he's——' she cleared her throat, 'he's got a girl-friend.'

The information appeared to fill Miles with pleasure. He smiled and lifted his half-finished glass of wine, said 'Cheers' and drank—alone.

As they drove away from the restaurant, Miles suggested that they might call on her parents. 'Your mother said she had been going to phone you, but your father wouldn't let her. Suzanne, why is there this quarrel between your father and your—husband?' Miles seemed to find it difficult to say the word.

How should she answer that without giving away any secrets? 'It—well, it goes back a long way,' she improvised, 'to when Ross wanted to marry me and my father refused permission. We did marry, as you know, but with the courts' permission instead.'

Cynthia welcomed her daughter as if she had been away for years. 'How are you getting on?' she asked.

Lucas's eyes darted towards Miles, then he asked his daughter briskly, 'Is your—*he* treating you properly?'

'Very *properly*, Father,' she answered, emphasising the double meaning.

'Sit down, dear,' Cynthia invited, 'I'll make you a coffee. Miles?'

'We had one after our meal, thanks, Mrs Cannon,' Miles declined, sitting next to Suzanne.

'Well now,' Lucas remarked, too heartily, 'it's great to see you two together. How far have you got with the divorce proceedings?' He addressed his last remark, in a harsher tone, to his daughter.

'In less than two days, and over the weekend?' she replied, which she felt was answer enough.

Lucas looked discomfited, retreating into his corner where the antique bureau stood. He plainly disliked being inhibited in his flow of invective against his son-in-law through the presence of the young man from whose father he so desperately needed assistance.

After a while, Suzanne felt restless. Thoughts of Ross were tugging her back to his home—which she was in danger of coming to regard as her home. 'Shall we go?' she asked Miles, and they stood up together.

Suzanne's mother hugged her. Lucas shook Miles by the hand and ignored his daughter. Suzanne felt her hands clench, but she told herself she did not care.

On the way back to Ross's house, she sat back in the car seat and closed her eyes. In her mind she heard again the words Ross had spoken earlier that day. 'Memories I'll keep,' he'd said, 'the happiness in your face after we'd made love, the way you smiled when we were together.' Most hurtful of all, he had told her that he wouldn't have married her if he'd met her now.

When she had used the same words to him, they had been spoken in anger. She simply hadn't meant them. Yet he had said them unemotionally. He had meant every single one.

Miles watched as she used her key. He followed her inside, then took her in his arms. A movement from nearby told her Ross was not far away, so with deliberation, she returned Miles' kiss. It cost her a great effort but she overcame her feeling of distaste. Her response was such that Miles raised his head to reveal a face glowing with pleasure.

For a few moments after the door had closed on him, Suzanne stood listening to the sound of his car driving away. Her eyes had remained down, studying the leather grain of her bag. When she did move, she slipped off her jacket and hung it on the banister post.

It was impossible to delay any longer meeting Ross's eyes. She had expected them to be cool, but not like pieces of ice. His words were like tightly-packed snowballs, stinging her face. 'You enjoyed that? You really enjoyed that apology for a kiss?'

Suzanne congratulated herself on her acting technique. She had hated it! Nothing would make her tell him. At the foot of the stairs, she stared back.

He was coming slowly nearer. 'It looks as though you've forgotten what it's like to be kissed by a man—a living, breathing man. Let me show you.'

A handful of paces separated them. She started up the stairs. Ross had moved more quickly than she had estimated and his arm was wound round her waist, lifting and tugging her back.

He dragged her backwards into the living area, turned her and pulled her to him. She was out of breath, but he did not care. His lips worked at hers until they parted and she knew the heady taste of him once more. Her mouth was his to do with it as he pleased, and it took more and more willingly his every onslaught.

Her eyes were closed as he swung her over his arm, his fingers unfastening the buttons of her dress. He was invading the privacy of her body, his roughened, moulding hands bringing her breasts to hardening life, a cry of pleasure to her throat.

His smile was one of victory caused, she guessed through the mistiness of her mind, by his easy conquest of her. I'm divorcing him, she told herself in panic. He hasn't conquered me, he mustn't be allowed to. The thought gave her strength and she started to struggle, tearing away from him at last. Her half-glazed eyes stared at him. Her hands lifted to her dishevelled hair, her breaths trying to even themselves out in her lungs.

Following his eyes after seeing his cynical smile, she realised how much of her was revealed through the opening of her dress. With shaking fingers, she pulled the gap shut, ran to the stairs and made it to the top.

In her bedroom, she sat head in hands thinking, over and over, I wanted him to go on. It doesn't matter that he's changed, I still love him. More now than ever before. So what am I to do? How can I divorce him knowing that I love him still?

When Suzanne walked into the shop next morning, Maggie Millet greeted her with relief. 'I wondered if you would come in,' she said. 'I knew you were moving house this weekend.'

Suzanne went behind the screen where Maggie had installed a small desk, plus a chair or two. Hanging up her jacket, she said, 'I'd have told you if I hadn't been able to make it. My——' the word still sounded too strange to say, 'Ross went off before I was even awake. I came in my new car.'

It all sounded so cosy, Suzanne realised with a shock.

Maggie must have thought so, too, since she asked, with surprise, 'Are you two back together again?' Suzanne had told her about Ross's sudden reappearance in her life, but not the exact reason for her own move into his house. Her explanation of this action had been vague, but she had never really got on with her father. Maggie had asked no questions.

'The answer's both yes and no,' Suzanne replied. 'The car was there in the garage and Ross told me I could use it. It doesn't mean,' she added hurriedly, 'that he bought it for me. And we do live separately——'

'Sorry, I shouldn't have asked the question in the first place. I'm just glad you came in.'

'Are you going off on your usual Monday morning buying spree?'

'Not this morning.' At Suzanne's look of surprise, Maggie went on, 'We've got so much stock, I'm running out of places to store it.'

Suzanne made a face, wondering what might be coming. When Maggie groaned, saying, 'I've been looking at the accounts, taking the figures apart and trying to make some sense of them,' Suzanne stopped wondering. She knew something was wrong.

Maggie glanced hopefully round the screen as if she thought she had heard a customer entering. The shop was empty. 'I'm sorry to have to say it, Suzanne, but the red light's flashing. Sales have been slow lately. Have you noticed?'

Suzanne's heart sank as she nodded. Maggie's business had hit troubled waters, just like her father's. There was no one to come to Maggie's aid. She was a widow and a businesswoman, with a house to pay for, so many things to worry about.

The savings she had shared with her late husband had been used to buy the shop. There was a loan outstanding from the bank. There was no perceptible hope in Maggie's eyes to show that she had received assurance from them that the period of the loan could be extended.

'Is it the end, then, Maggie? You'll have to close down?'

Maggie pulled a chair forward and sat down, telling Suzanne to do the same. 'I'll give it a couple more weeks, I'll have to. If we could sell two or three of the larger items, like the pine dining table and chairs or the bookcase, it would go some way towards helping us over this bad patch.'

'It wouldn't be the real answer, would it?' Suzanne prompted gently. 'The rent for the shop has to be paid, plus the rates and so on.'

'Don't remind me,' Maggie pleaded, putting a hand to her head. Her blonde hair was carefully dressed, her slim figure looking trim in a dark two-piece suit.

The door bell rang. Maggie was on her feet in a few

seconds. Returning, she said she had sold a pine magazine rack. 'Maybe it's a good omen,' she laughed, seizing
a duster and preparing to go round the stock with it.

Three other customers patronised the shop that day,
buying small items. Pulling down the door blind, Maggie
sighed. 'If things go on like this, the end's in sight.'

'It's been a dull day,' Suzanne tried soothing her. 'If
the sun shines tomorrow, perhaps it will make people
take out their credit cards or cheque books.'

Maggie smiled, but it had obviously been an effort.

As Suzanne drove home that evening—Ross's home,
she kept reminding herself—she wondered if she should
cook for two, and if so, at what time would she be
expected to serve the meal?

When she opened the door of the garage, she found
Ross's car already there. Excitement and apprehension
fought inside her as she attempted to visualise the kind
of welcome, if any, she would receive.

Opening the door and entering the house, a pleasant
smell of cooking wafted into her nostrils. Ross was preparing the meal! How many, she wondered, was he
cooking for? Himself, leaving her to cope with her own?
If so, she couldn't grumble, since their ways of life were
to be divided.

It seemed he regarded living separately in a different
light. The dining-table, she noted, as she looked through
the living-room and into the alcove, was set for two.
Was she to be one of the two, or was he expecting a
guest?

He turned briefly as she stood in the kitchen doorway.
He did not smile in answer to hers. 'Who—who are you
cooking for?' she ventured. 'For yourself, or——?'

'For both of us. Do you really think I'd be so petty as
to cook just for myself? If you'd come home first, what
would you have done?'

'Cooked for us both.'

'So why should you assume I would do otherwise?'

'I—I just thought you might be expecting a guest.'

He turned and was smiling, even if there was a touch

of mockery. 'Be my guest.' She laughed. 'After all,' he went on, 'we might be living separate lives, but that fact surely doesn't stop us from offering a crumb or two to the other when they come home hungry at the end of the day.'

Suzanne smiled. 'Can I give you a hand?'

'No, thanks.' His tone was cooler now. 'Living in the wilder places of the world forces you to be self-sufficient. I learnt the hard way, through necessity. Go and do whatever you want to do, and we'll eat.'

She needed no second bidding. Having eaten only a small lunch with Maggie at a local café, she felt in need of a refill to bring back her energy.

Ross served the meal the moment she reappeared, and Suzanne looked at her plate, noting its contents with astonishment. It was a savoury pie. 'How did you get this ready in such a short time?' she asked.

'Prepared most of the ingredients yesterday evening while you were out.' He produced a bottle of wine, holding it up for her approval. She nodded, still overcome by his achievement. 'I put it in the fridge, then I returned home early for once and cooked the meal. I hope your tastes haven't changed. It's liver and bacon pie. I assumed you'd like it, but then I was judging by the old days.' He poured the wine, drank a little and started eating.

Suzanne ate silently for a while, recalling the fun they had had in the old kitchen at the shared house, how they had to fight for the use of the cooking stove and wade through other people's unwashed dishes to wash their own.

'No, my tastes haven't changed,' she said at last.

Their eyes met and parted. There was a long silence while they ate the food. Replete, Suzanne stretched and smiled. 'That was great, Ross.'

Again their eyes came together, clashing. His dropped to her shape which was exposed briefly by her uplifted arms. Colouring, she lowered them, embarrassingly aware of having behaved in a too-familiar way. Easing back her chair, she stood up, anxious to escape from the feeling of having done something she shouldn't.

He stood too, as polite as if she were really his guest. His courtesy aroused in her an irrational fury. *I'm your wife*, she wanted to tell him. But what was the use?

'There's fresh fruit.' He indicated the wooden dish on the sideboard. 'Would you like an apple?'

The shiny skins, the irresistible 'apple' smell attracted and invited teeth to bite them. Suzanne nodded, damping down her anger at his attitude. 'I'll take it up to my bedroom.'

'I've made coffee for two. It's almost ready. Then,' with a meaningful look, 'there are the dishes to wash.'

Subsiding into her chair, she nodded, glad that she did not have to run from him. 'I get it. You cooked the meal, I do the dishes.'

His smile met hers, fleetingly. 'You're quick to catch on.'

He sat beside her on the couch, having served her with coffee. She became overwhelmingly conscious of him, trying to visualise the mature solidity of his body, which had once been so thin, beneath the blue shirt he was wearing.

His dark blue tie was still in place, his suit trousers were perfectly tailored, yet, seated as he was, taut across his broad hips. Although her eyes were closed as she rested her head against the couch back, she felt the pull of him.

Even without his jacket, the executive air lingered. His dark hair was still neatly combed, lying partly across his forehead. There were, she noted, opening her eyes and finding that his were now shut, faint lines raying from his eyes and across his forehead.

Six years they had lost, gone for ever, six years of growing closer, having fun, having children. She wanted to cry for them, stamp her feet, bang her fists to get them back, like a child wanting something that had been taken from it.

Now, soon, Ross would be taken from her by the

slow but inexorable processes of the law. And by a cruel lash of irony, it would be she who would have to initiate them, go to a lawyer, tell a lie and say, 'I want to divorce my husband.'

'Did you call on your parents today?'

His voice jerked her from the morass of her thoughts. 'No, Miles and I went there last night. Today I went to work.'

She felt the vibrations of his increase in tension at the knowledge of where she had been with Miles the evening before. He did not look at her, but said, 'You told Harringdon nothing about the loan, I hope?' He emptied his coffee cup and put it down.

'Nothing.' She drank her coffee, too, and watched him refill both cups.

There was a long silence while they drank again. At last she said, to make conversation, 'Maggie Millet's worried.'

'Don't tell me,' he commented in a here-we-go-again tone, 'her business is in financial difficulties.'

'It's not a joke.' Suzanne leaned forward with a thump, deposited cup on saucer. 'She's got a mortgage, a business to run and no husband. Plus a bank loan to pay interest on.'

His head turned lazily towards her, his eyelids drooping. 'I have heard it all before.'

Suzanne stood up. 'I'm sorry if I'm boring you, and I'm sorry if it gets monotonous, but it happens to be true. Maggie doesn't know which way to turn. We've been talking about it nearly all day. Now I *am* going upstairs.'

She looked round for her bag, only to find a grip of iron squeezing her fingers and pulling her back to the couch. Her hand burned at the touch of him and she sat reluctantly, jerking her fingers free. 'Don't touch me,' her glare was saying as they met his hard, penetrating look. Dismayed, she was sure she had seen a flash of challenge in his blue eyes.

His hand reached out again, taking hers for the

second time. It was as if he was making sure she would not try another getaway tactic. 'If the shop closed, it would mean you were out of a job?'

'That's obvious, isn't it?' she returned sourly. 'I'd hate it, just hanging around here with only my basket-work ...' She paused, having realised the futility of that activity if Maggie didn't want her stuff. 'Not even that, with no retail outlet.'

'I've told you, you don't need to work.'

'And be financially dependent on you? No, thank you!'

Ross stood up and wandered to the window overlooking the drive and the front garden. 'When are you going to see the solicitor? Tomorrow?'

'Are you so eager to get rid of me?' Her ears told her the question had been childish, which was probably why he had ignored it. 'Weekdays, I'm working.'

'You'll have to take a morning off, won't you?'

He really did want her to go! 'I can't desert Maggie at the moment. She needs me there in case something turns up to take her out of the shop.' Suzanne knew this was unlikely and reproached herself for having let him put her in the position of making excuses for not consulting a solicitor.

It was lucky, she thought, that he could not see into her heart. It would have told him that there was nothing in the world she wanted more than to run back into his arms and stay there for ever.

'Tell me when you're going,' Ross directed. 'I shall then go to my solicitor and file an "answer", where I put my side of the case.'

'That will make it more difficult for me,' she replied agitatedly, 'although it won't stop the divorce, not after all these years. It would only be out of spite, Ross. Why bother to defend it?'

His back stayed to her. 'My intention is to delay matters.'

'But why?' She was standing now. 'Don't bother to answer. To have your revenge for what I did six years ago.' He did not respond. 'I had to stay behind, Ross.' Her voice was thickening, to her annoyance. 'I was truly afraid for my mother. And now I've got to divorce you so that my father can have a more permanent form of financial assistance, instead of the temporary loan you've given him.'

He swung round, his face twisted, the anger he had contained erupting. 'You hate your father's guts.'

'No, no, I don't. You've got it wrong.'

'I had it wrong six years ago and I've got it wrong now? The real "wrong" was in ever marrying you.' His whole body had hardened into angles. Suzanne felt sickened and shaken by his words. 'Such loyalty you have, my dear.' He was standing in front of her. 'Loyalty to everybody but your husband, to whom you owe first loyalty.'

Her eyes filled, her hand came out, shaking, towards him. He grasped it and threw it down. A few strides took him from the room, a few more and he was gone from the house.

When she went downstairs, dressed for work, Suzanne discovered that Ross had again left early, after breakfasting.

Making herself toast and coffee, plus a few sandwiches to eat for lunch, she drove to the shop. There was a reined excitement in Maggie as she greeted her. 'I've got to go out this morning. You'll mind the shop, won't you?' she asked.

Smiling, Suzanne nodded. It was probably her boyfriend she was meeting. He had been abroad for some months. Dan had only gone, Maggie had told her, so as to push up his earnings. Maybe she was hoping to get help from him. Since Maggie did not let her into the secret, she didn't like to ask.

There were no customers all morning. By the time Suzanne turned the sign to 'closed for lunch', she was weary with waiting for the shop's entrance bell to ring. Taking out a magazine, she read it while eating her sandwiches. She had put away her flask of coffee when there was a rattling of the entrance door handle.

Reaching out for the mirror and powder compact which she kept in a drawer, Suzanne tidied herself. Putting on her saleswoman's smile, she emerged from behind the screen to find Maggie holding open the door for a customer.

He was tall, he was solid as a pillar of stone, his hair was dark and he had piercing blue eyes. And he was smiling with sardonic amusement at Suzanne, who stared up at him unbelievingly.

Maggie looked up at Ross. 'This is the man I went to meet.' She put both her arms around one of his. 'He's the most wonderful man, your husband,' she was saying. 'Know what he's going to do?' Dumbly, Suzanne shook her head. 'He's offered to buy my business!'

'You haven't!' Suzanne exclaimed, clasping her hands.

'I have.' His smile became a grin.

'He's going to get an accountant in to look at the books. He's going to have the business and everything valued, and he's going to make me an offer. I've told him that as long as he offers me the purchase price plus inflation, he can have it.'

'Which makes Mrs Millet no businesswoman,' Ross remarked, smiling down at the woman who still clung to him.

'Aren't you pleased, Suzanne?' Maggie asked. Suzanne found herself unable to say a word. 'If not for your own sake, then for mine?'

At last Suzanne nodded, making her lips move. 'Delighted, Maggie.' She was still too dazed to say more.

'Thanks for telling him last night what a mess I was in,' Maggie went on. 'He said he had a good think about it and came to a decision. Well,' she let out a tremendous sigh of relief, 'he wants to look round the shop, inspect the goods. Like to show him round?' She offered Suzanne Ross's arm. 'He's yours, after all.'

'No, thanks, Maggie.' Ross was staring through the display windows to the busy street as if assessing the shop's situation. 'I'd rather you acted as my guide and saleswoman.'

Maggie looked uncertainly at Suzanne. 'Yes. Well, I suppose I am the owner and you're the possible buyer.' She led Ross away.

Suzanne stood in the centre of the shop, hands clasped, looking every inch the perfect and patient sales assistant. Inside, she was in a state of rebellion. Did Ross need to be so high-handed in his attitude towards her? She could have shown him round quite as efficiently as Maggie, yet he had cold-bloodedly rejected her.

As she stood watching them, she willed a customer in, but not a single person looked in the windows. Ross was examining closely a gatelegged table made of pine. He was nodding as Maggie talked, probably telling of its origin in the workshop of the hopeful craftsman who had made it.

Nearby, there was a pinewood desk, crafted by yet another local maker. Ross pulled and shut the drawers, ran fingertips over the smooth surfaces and nodded again. Suzanne frowned. What was he up to?

Maggie led the way back, past Suzanne. Ross did not look at her, his eyes being too busy inspecting the state of the decorations. 'We're going to examine the stock upstairs,' Maggie announced. 'While we're there, sell the entire contents to the horde of customers outside, won't you?' Maggie grinned and they climbed the wooden stairs.

Two people did come in, a middle-aged couple in search, Suzanne discovered to her delight, of one of the larger items. That dining-table over there, they said, plus the six matching dining chairs. By the time Maggie led Ross back into the shop, the couple were paying for the things they had bought. Maggie's eyebrows nearly reached the ceiling as she went behind the screen to talk to Ross.

When they had gone, Maggie put her head round the

screen. Suzanne nodded and her employer let out a whoop of joy.

'Your husband's been spending a fortune, too,' she told Suzanne, who was watching Ross writing out a large cheque. 'One gatelegged table, one desk and upstairs, the patio set of two basket chairs, table and couch. You do realise,' Maggie explained to Ross, 'that they're not for all-weather use. So,' to Suzanne, 'remind him to bring them in when it rains.'

'Well,' Ross commented, replacing his pen, 'your sales seem to have picked up so much, maybe you don't need my help at all.'

His smile was slow, directed at Suzanne, who received it with a frozen expression. Maggie missed it and exclaimed, 'Oh, but I do. Days like this happen so rarely I've forgotten the last time.'

'I was only joking,' Ross assured her, and she sighed thankfully. 'Now, back to business. I'll contact my accountant and explain the situation. I'll get him to phone you to arrange a time for him to call. There will have to be a valuation and so on. You understand, Maggie?'

'Yes, Ross.' Maggie smiled broadly at Suzanne. 'We decided on first names. Hope you don't mind, Suzanne?' Suzanne, who did mind, very much, said of course she didn't.

By the time Suzanne let herself into the house that evening, she had a battalion of words lined up in her mind with which to attack the opposition. The house was dauntingly empty. The enemy was missing and his absence left her feeling empty, too.

Last night he had cooked for her. Tonight she would cook for him. He had not told her about his weekday eating habits or his hours of work. She just had to assume that, having an office job, he followed a reasonably regular pattern of arrival and departure. If he was making up for the time he had spent in the shop that morning, then she would keep his food warm in the oven.

Four hours later, it was still in the oven, but it was no

longer warm. Her spirits had long ago flagged, her battalion of words dispersed. Too unsettled to go to bed, she looked outside and saw the moon sitting high against the starlit blackness of infinity. Without pausing to find a jacket, she stepped through the patio doors.

Making her way down the steps in the lawn with the help of the moon's light, she stood at the side of the swimming pool. It was mirror-smooth in the windless evening, streaked now and then with silver as a night insect disturbed it. All around, the green of the trees and bushes were paled and cool.

A swimming pool at the end of the garden—it was something they had never even dreamed of in that first and only real year of their marriage. Now it was there, had it made anybody any happier? Did Ross take a swim for exercise before breakfast? Did the unlimited amount of money he seemed to possess give him a feeling of power, of satisfaction?

So many questions she wanted to ask, but not of the Ross who had returned into her life. It was the other Ross she had known, had loved hopelessly, that she wanted to find. She sighed, knowing that even if she searched for him for the rest of her life, she would seek him in vain.

The cool hands round her upper arms gave her a terrible fright. Crying out, she put a hand to her chest as if to still her racing heartbeats. Her entire system was shaken to its foundations. Her head moved as she tried to find somewhere to put it.

Blindly she turned, clutching at Ross's sleeves, feeling his strong hand urge her head to find a resting place between the edges of his jacket and against his chest. 'How could you,' she whispered, her body trembling, 'how could you frighten me so?'

'I thought you'd heard me coming.' His voice was a deep, echoing sound beneath her ear.

Her arms found their way under the jacket and around his waist. Her eyes closed and she let her head move with the rhythm of his breathing. A curious relaxation released her from the dreadful tension—tension not just arising from the fright, but which seemed to have hoarded itself over the empty years.

After a long time, hours, she thought, she spoke into his chest, 'I cooked a meal for you and kept it warm, but it's cold now.'

Ross lifted her head away and raised her chin. 'I'm sorry. It was one of those things.'

'And because I'm divorcing you,' she sought his eyes, but they were in shadow, 'you didn't think it was worth bothering to let me know?'

He seemed to regard the question as not worth answering. Instead, his head lowered slowly, his jaw, square and stubborn, coming nearer. His kiss was gentle, a small kiss like a wine-tasting. Then it hardened and he drank deeply, his mouth probing the depths of hers, their bodies fitting together as if each belonged to the other.

When he eased his mouth away, he looked into her uplifted, desperate eyes and asked, 'Will you sleep with me?'

The idea was so sweet she swayed, but she cried, 'No, no, I mustn't! I'm divorcing you.'

'To hell with the divorce! We're a man and a woman who want each other. You must have slept with other men during those years apart. Regard me, if you like, as one of those men.'

'There've been no other men.' Panic was making her hands moist. With all her strength she pulled free and walked quickly towards the house. He was close behind her, finally overtaking her. He strode through the opened glass doors and made for the drinks, pouring himself one. Busily, she closed the doors and secured them, turning to watch as he threw the drink down his throat.

Her legs felt so weak, she would have to rest before climbing the stairs. Shakily she sat down, elbow resting on the chair arm, head on her hand. She had needed him, wanted him so much that the longing had caused pain to encase her, like a plaster after an accident.

Ross sat down, too, holding the empty glass on the arm of the chair, while his head rested back. His face was pale, his expression forbidding. Finally Suzanne flopped back, eyes closed.

'Why did you decide to help Maggie?' she asked, her voice heavy with fatigue and strain. He did not answer. She persisted, 'When I told you about her troubles, I didn't do so expecting you to rush to help her. I don't expect you to act the big-hearted philanthropist to all the poor and needy people I know.' It was, she realised, a hurtful thing to say, but she had wanted to hurt him as he was hurting her all the time.

He did not lift his head, but Suzanne watched the area around his mouth go white. 'I've heard of ingratitude,' he answered bitingly, 'but none so blatant as the sort you've just handed out. In fact,' he stood now and seized her wrist, pulling her up and forcing her arm behind her, 'if my upbringing hadn't made me into such a gentleman,' the words gritted from his clenched jaw, 'I'd strip you, throw you into my bed and not let you go until you begged at my feet for mercy.'

Suzanne endured the pain from her bent arm, determined not to weaken. She had taken verbal onslaughts from her father that had pained her, but none like this.

In those joyous first months of marriage, Ross had touched her only to love, never to hurt. When he let her go, she could not prevent a gasp from escaping, although she did not want this hard stranger's pity. Staggering to the door, she turned to hurl her anger at him.

The sight of his back towards her and his hands raking raggedly through his hair checked her lips even as they began to move in accusation.

# CHAPTER SEVEN

BEFORE going into work, Suzanne called the solicitor's office and made an appointment to see him. No sooner had she put down the phone than it rang again.

'Miles!' she exclaimed as if she had not seen him for days. She was still reacting to the fact that she had taken an irrevocable stride away from Ross. She had not meant to sound so pleased to hear from him.

'Will you come out with me this evening, Suzanne?' There was only the briefest pause before she answered 'yes'. 'I wish,' Miles remarked wistfully, 'you could entertain me at home like you did at your parents' house.'

'I agree,' Suzanne replied, 'that it's a nuisance we always have to go out nowadays, but there's no alternative, Miles. Ross wouldn't allow——'

'But you're divorcing the man!'

'Which reminds me,' Suzanne sidetracked quickly, 'I've made an appointment to see Mr Webster the day after tomorrow. In the morning.'

'So you're getting the divorce started at last!' Miles sounded delighted.

'Ross keeps saying he's going to defend. That will prolong the proceedings,' she told him.

'You'll get it eventually, though.'

'Yes.' Suzanne felt her voice go flat. 'Must go, Miles. You'll call for me, usual time?'

Arriving at the shop nearly an hour late, Suzanne apologised to Maggie, explaining the reason.

'You really are divorcing him, then? Why, Suzanne, for heaven's sake? He's great, he's a dream man! All that solidity and not an ounce of fat, all lean flesh and muscle.' Maggie rolled her eyes expressively. 'You wouldn't get me slicing myself apart from a man like him!'

Suzanne hooked her coat on the wall, her back to Maggie. 'All the love's gone. What's the use of staying married?'

'Gone from you or from him?'

I can't give anything away, Suzanne thought desolately. 'He's got a—a woman friend. That's what he called her. Met her in Africa. She's qualified in his own subject. They chose his furnishings together, which means she must have come back from Africa with him.'

'Ah.' Maggie was thoughtful. 'But he's defending the case, you said. It just doesn't make sense.'

'To make things difficult, that's all.' Maggie looked unconvinced. 'Out of revenge for my not having gone abroad with him six years ago. Don't shake your head, Maggie. It's true.'

Maggie gazed out from behind the screen. 'All I know is,' she said, 'that his offering to buy me out, yet let me stay on here, is one of the kindest things anyone's ever done for me in my life.'

Suzanne's head drooped a little as she sorted through magazines on the desk. 'Kind' was something Ross had never been to her. Passionate, demanding, tender when it suited him—the memories were turning sour already, she realised—but never kind. Would she have wanted him to be? her inner self asked.

Maggie was serving a customer. Having made a sale, she returned behind the screen with an enthusiasm which Suzanne tried to catch but failed.

'The accountants have phoned,' Maggie told her. 'Ross's accountants. They're coming tomorrow morning. How's that for speed? Does everyone dance to your husband's tune?' she added, laughing.

'Don't keep calling him that!'

At the sight of Maggie's consternation, Suzanne at once regretted her irritability. 'Sorry, Maggie—I'm on edge.'

Her employer nodded understandingly, but could not keep the happiness from her eyes. The answer to Maggie's question, had Suzanne responded to it, would have been, Yes, even my father, which I still find difficult to believe.

There was no smell of cooking to greet her that evening, though having seen Ross's car in the garage, she knew he was home. Eventually she found him wandering in the garden, and he turned as she watched him from the patio doors. He seemed unsurprised by her presence.

'Is it my turn to cook for us?' she asked, uncertain of the situation.

'I'm eating out. Cook for yourself. Or there's salad in the fridge.'

'Thanks, but I'm eating out, too.'

He looked at her quickly, apparently gleaned from her expression who her escort would be and turned away, walking down to stare into the blue-tinted pool. Her feet took her to join him. He looked at her reflection, she at his. If she bent down and tried to touch his image, all she would have had was a handful of water slipping away. Which was about all the substance of him she had ever had, she thought.

'That furniture you bought from Maggie's shop,' she remarked, as if it had just occurred to her, 'where will it go?'

His shoulders lifted and he stared through his own reflection. 'Various places.'

'In some of those empty rooms in the modern part?'

'Probably,' he replied, and left her staring at her own blurring, undulating reflection.

Suzanne heard Ross slam out of the house as she was getting ready for Miles. As she slipped on her sandals, she realised she had forgotten to tell him of her coming visit to the solicitor. This evening, when she and Miles got back to the house, she would tell Ross. He himself would surely have returned by then.

He had not. His space in the garage was empty when Miles parked in the drive and Suzanne checked up. Sliding back into the passenger seat, she told Miles he could come in with her for a few minutes, if he liked. For coffee or a drink . . .

'No, thanks, I'd rather not.'

'But you said this morning you wished you could come in afterwards like when I lived with my parents.' With astonishment, she watched Miles shaking his head. Was he *afraid* of Ross?

'He might come back unexpectedly,' Miles objected, 'and then——'

'And then he'd beat you up?' Suzanne could not stop the laughter bubbling out of her. 'Ross isn't the hitting kind, Miles,' she added gently.

'He is, with his tongue. He's the sort who can tear the guts out of you with words.'

Suzanne thought, He's right there. He can reduce you to pulp, if you let him. Miles got out and Suzanne asked where he was going. He opened the door to the back seat. 'Come and sit beside me,' he invited.

'You mean——' she could hardly believe it, 'make love on the back seat?' Was he being serious?

'I know it's not ideal,' he glanced at the unlighted house, 'but it's better than the possibility of being interrupted.'

Still unbelieving, Suzanne got out and stepped into the rear of the car. 'I'd much rather not, Miles.'

'Just a kiss or two.' Miles' voice had turned pleading. 'We are supposed to be kind of engaged, aren't we? And I haven't kissed you all evening.'

Holding herself stiffly, Suzanne waited, unable to soften her attitude towards the man whose wife everybody accepted she would one day become. Unabashed, he put his arms round her, pulling her against him in a half-lying position. His kissed her closed lips, but no matter how hard he tried, she could not relax. For a moment he stopped, as if to regain his breath.

Lying back with her eyes closed, Suzanne attempted to reassure him, and in so doing, tried to persuade herself that what she was saying was true. 'It'll be different when I'm free of——' Ross, she had nearly said, but she would never be free of him, 'free of this marriage, after the divorce.'

Miles' lips slid across her cheek to her mouth again and he murmured, 'I know how it is, Suzanne. You're on edge. Well, so am I, but it's nice just to kiss you.'

A car crackled over the pebbled drive, hooting. Miles' car was blocking the way to the garage. There was a slam of a door, the stride of angry feet, a shadowy, infuriated face at the window. Then it had gone. Suzanne tried to drag herself from Miles' hold, marvelling at the remarkable strength of his arms.

'I'd better go,' she said, 'and you'd better move. Thanks for the meal and—and——' she couldn't bring herself to pretend an enjoyment of his kisses, 'see you again soon.' She leant across and placed a hasty, soothing kiss on his cheek. It seemed to please him in spite of its being a meaningless gesture.

With a wave, she let herself into the house, hoping to escape upstairs before Ross had finished locking the garage. As usual, he was too fast for her. He must have moved like a panther to gain on her. Halfway up, she turned, feeling the power of him slow her down, bringing her climb to an abrupt stop.

His black outline in the unilluminated hall was an alarming sight. He had the choice of either coming after her, or compelling her to descend. She felt the fury raying from him. It was curling round her body like a whip, impelling her down. He had no right to push and pull her any more, nor had he any right to be angry with her. They were divorcing each other, weren't they?

'Come down and join me,' he ordered.

'No, thank you. I'm tired, I'm going to bed.' Turning, she made a dash for it, but did not even reach her room.

He caught her arms and fixed them behind her, looking coldly into her blazing eyes. 'Where do you want to entertain me—in your bedroom or downstairs in the living-room? If it's the first, I'll know what's expected of me. If it's the second, I'll guess that you've chosen the more subtle approach.'

Suzanne tried to struggle free. 'I don't know what you're talking about.'

Ross compelled her towards her room. 'No? Then it's time we renewed our—acquaintance.' He eyed her low-necked dress, the inviting shape beneath it.

With his foot he pushed at the half-opened door. 'Not my bedroom,' she answered hastily. 'If I must go with you somewhere, let it be the living-room.'

His smile held derision, knowing the reason for her decision. He released her arms, putting the palm of his hand to her back to urge her down the stairs. In the living-room, her legs felt unsteady but she refused to allow herself to sit down. It would put her on a lower level.

As his biting voice came at her, she told herself she needn't have worried, since it seemed she could hardly be lower in his estimation, anyway, no matter what she did.

'What the hell were you doing with Harringdon?' he gritted. 'Aren't you both too old to behave like a couple of teenagers petting in the back of a car?'

'I can do what I like now, Ross. When I agreed to come back and live with you—separately, as you said—I did so under duress. I was an instrument of barter in exchange for a loan. I certainly didn't make a vow to give up all—all other men until the divorce finally comes through.'

'Any more than I promised to give up other women.' Did he know how much he could hurt her with such words? 'But when I take out another woman with a view to an evening of lovemaking to follow, I take her to an appropriate place. I don't just grope in the back of a car.'

'You won't let me take him upstairs!' His lips became a thin line. He believed that that was what she really wanted to do? If so, it couldn't be denied that she had put the implication there herself.

'So he'll just have to pay for the use of a bed, won't he? In some hotel, out in the countryside where you won't be recognised.'

'You make it sound so—so degrading.'

'And isn't it, when you're a married woman?'

'What about your being a married man? You're trying to make two sets of rules, one for men, one for——'

'Wives. I didn't make them up. They exist. In nature, they exist. I know they're often broken, but that's not my fault. I'm merely asking that you curb your *passion* for each other,' he mocked the word, 'until my wedding ring is off your finger.'

She had to hit back at him somehow. Then she remembered what he had made her promise to tell him. 'That shouldn't be long now,' she responded, with a flash of satisfaction. 'I'm seeing my solicitor the day after tomorrow and starting divorce proceedings. You did ask me to tell you,' she ended defensively.

'Thanks.' Ross removed his jacket and threw it across a chair, then slowly closed the gap between them. 'I'll contact my own lawyer and file an answer.' His hands held her waist. 'Let's drink to our final separation.' There was a glint in his eyes and it struck a chord of misery inside her. He was willing to toast their coming parting!

'No, thank you.' The feel of his hands as they tightened round her waist at her answer made her want to fling herself at him. I belong to you, she longed to cry, can't you feel how my whole being is responding to you?

'So the idea of splitting with me doesn't please you? Would you rather we stayed together? Would you rather——' he pulled her against him, 'be loving me than leaving me?'

His hand moved to secure the back of her head, clamping her mouth to his, while his other arm coiled round her to rest low-down on her opposite hip. The familiarity of the action, the way he pressed her closer so that she could feel the throbbing maleness of him, started to melt the layer of protective ice around her heart. It had been there for six long years.

Her arms reached up to wrap around his neck. She gave him her mouth, lips parted, offering no barrier to prevent the partial fusion of them into one being. Ross took his hand from her head and swung her shoulder partly away, while his lips stayed against hers. His hand cupped the firmness of her breasts then, irritated by the barrier presented by the material of the dress, untied a ribbon at her neck.

You're mine, claimed his caressing, trailing fingers over her tingling flesh, I know everything about you . . . my body is clamouring for yours . . .

At the moment her instincts began answering his, like a female calling to its mate in the high reaches of a forest, he lifted his head, but his eyes stayed warm. 'Well? Will you come to me tonight?'

Even as she shook her head and stumbled as he thrust her from him, she felt the heart of her torn away. 'Not tonight, Ross, nor any night. Our marriage is over. I'm divorcing you, so conjugal bliss is out.'

Lips thinning, eyes on fire, he reached for her, but the telephone rang, breaking the tension. He dropped her arm and went to silence the bell. She rubbed the place where he had gripped her.

Ross returned, saying tonelessly, 'It's for you. Maggie wants a word.'

'Suzanne, so sorry to call you so late, but I tried earlier—no reply. It's about tomorrow. I told you the accountants are coming in the morning, didn't I? Well, it seems they're likely to be here all day, so I've decided to close the shop. Don't bother to come in, will you? Has Ross told you the furniture will be arriving in the afternoon?'

'He didn't tell me, but thanks for letting me know.'

They chatted for a few minutes, then cut off.

Suzanne walked slowly back, to find Ross sitting, eyes closed, legs fully stretched, in a chair.

'Where do you want the furniture to go?' she asked dully.

He surfaced as if he had been deep in thought. 'The furniture?' He spoke as if he didn't care. 'I'll show you.' Pulling himself upright, he motioned her upstairs.

'Through to the modern part,' he directed, following her.

Opening the dividing door, she paused. 'Where now?'

He passed her, his eyes inscrutable as their bodies touched momentarily when he went by. He led the way past the furnished office and other bedrooms to an empty room. 'The desk will go here,' he indicated, 'under the window. The table against a wall, wherever you choose.' He looked down at her. 'Are you still making your mats and baskets?' Suzanne nodded. 'Then you can have this room as your work-place, if you like.'

She frowned. How far into the future was he looking? 'I'm not staying here for ever, Ross. It's a kind thought on your part, but——'

'Does it matter? It's yours for a few months or a few years.' His tone was dismissive and he went from the room, inviting her to follow.

There was another empty room next door. 'This room I plan one day to make into a nursery.'

Suzanne's heart jolted. Her nod was automatic. Her thoughts were going crazy. Which woman did he plan to make the mother of his children? It couldn't possibly be herself, since he knew that, fight the divorce though he might, before many months had passed they would be parted irrevocably.

This left only one possibility—that he had remarriage in mind as soon as the divorce was through—marriage to his girl-friend. So why fight the divorce? The answer came as unhesitatingly as it always did—to make things difficult for her in order to satisfy his craving for revenge.

'I see,' she managed to answer, turning away and walking stiffly back. He walked beside her. 'Where will the patio suite go when they deliver it?'

'Outside, while the weather holds. When it rains, there's a shed where the furniture can be stored.' Through the dividing door, his hand on her arm stopped her outside her bedroom. 'One thing I have to mention. You might have noticed I don't have a housekeeper.'

'I've been wondering about that.' Fascinated, she watched him remove his tie and unfasten his shirt buttons, revealing a patch of dark chest hair. Once she had rested her cheek against it, nestling up to him . . .

'Or,' he was saying, 'we could advertise and you could make the choice.'

'Or—what?' Suzanne shook her head to drive out the memories and return to the present. 'Sorry.'

'I was saying,' he repeated with a touch of irritation, 'that I'd been told about the woman, a Mrs Hadley, who used to housekeep here for the previous owner. It seems she'd be willing to come back.'

Suzanne nodded vigorously. 'I'd be pleased to have her here. If I were given the job of choosing, whoever comes——' she had difficulty in clearing the huskiness, 'after me might not like her.'

'Whoever comes after you,' he responded with a half-smile, 'might not like Mrs Hadley.'

'That's a chance we'll have to take, isn't it?' she answered sharply, immediately regretting having allowed her edginess to show. 'Whoever fills that nursery for you will probably demand a nanny, too.'

She swung to her own door to hide her trembling lips, calling over her shoulder, 'Goodnight.' Before closing the door, she counted three, but no request or demand came from him to gain entry, nor did a hand on her shoulder pull her back for a final kiss.

Lifting her head high, she walked resolutely across the room and told herself she would be counting every waking hour which took her towards the next day but one—and the beginning of freedom.

Freedom from what? her restless self asked between fretful periods of sleep. A legal document, a few strokes of a pen could never bring her freedom from loving the person who meant the most to her in all the world.

Heavy-eyed, she stirred at her usual time, although she would be spending the day at home—at Ross's home, she corrected herself quickly. Pulling on a towelling robe, she was crossing to the bathroom when Ross emerged from his room.

He was dressed for work, looked immaculate and remote. 'You'll be able to cope with the delivery of the furniture?' he asked, his glance taking in her tumbled appearance and darkly shadowed eyes.

Suzanne pulled her robe more closely around her, only to realise, by his examining gaze that, with the action, she had drawn attention to her shape. 'Yes, thank you,' she replied, taking her polite tone from him.

As she turned away, she realised there was something she had to ask. 'When—if—you buy Maggie's business,' she hated having virtually to beg from him, 'would there be any objection if I continued to be—to be employed by——'

'The new owner?' he took her up with cool amusement. 'None at all. As long as you accept that we'll have to negotiate your salary.'

'Why?' Her brown eyes widened. 'Couldn't I carry on being paid the wages that Maggie's been paying me?'

Ross laughed briefly. 'Sure. Why not? I did begin to think that you might get the idea that with your husband as boss, you'd be able to entice some more pay out of him.'

Her gaze grew earnest. 'After the——' she moistened her lips, 'after the divorce, would you still keep me on?'

A sheet of ice came down between them. 'I'll fire you the moment the divorce becomes absolute.' With one hand in his jacket pocket he walked away.

Suzanne was no sooner dry from her shower than the telephone rang. Remembering the extension in her bedroom, she darted across, tying the belt of the robe, and picked up the receiver.

'Suzanne dear, how are you getting on?'

'Mother? It's so good to hear from you. Are you okay, Mum?'

'Why shouldn't I be, dear?' Her mother sounded puzzled. 'I was hoping for a short chat just before you went off to work.'

'I've got a day off,' Suzanne explained. 'Can we meet somewhere?'

'Would Ross mind terribly if I came over? I haven't seen his house and I hear it's very pleasant.'

'Ross has gone to work. I'm sure he wouldn't mind. When will you be here?' Coffee time, her mother promised, and rang off.

Suzanne had showed her mother over the house, omitting to take her through to the modern extension. She merely pointed it out, hoping her mother would leave it at that.

Now they were talking over coffee and Mrs Cannon was praising everything about the place. 'I have one dearest wish, Suzanne,' her mother said, her tired eyes shining. Putting down her cup, she leaned forward to whisper, 'Don't tell your father, but I wish very much that you could stay with Ross for ever.'

'But Mother,' Suzanne's heart beat heavily, 'what about Father's business? He needs long-term financial help, doesn't he—not just the temporary loan Ross has given him.'

Cynthia Cannon gave an unworldly shrug of her thin shoulders. 'What do material things matter when placed against the stability of a truly loving relationship?'

'You think Ross and I have just that?' Cynthia nodded eagerly. 'Sorry, Mum.' Suzanne looked down at her own restless hands. 'We haven't got any kind of relationship.'

'That's because he's holding back, dear,' Cynthia asserted, now as worldly-wise as she was the opposite a few moments before. 'He knows you want a divorce and he's so considerate he's restraining himself from showing his love for you. He did say you would live separately, didn't he?'

Suzanne smiled at her mother's romanticising, and it turned into gentle laughter when she recalled Ross's ungentle and frequent breaking down of the physical barriers between them.

Cynthia looked a little bewildered. 'He is considerate, isn't he? I mean, he is respecting your privacy? There isn't anything in the way of your getting a divorce?'

Suzanne sighed deeply. 'A minute ago you were saying you wished I could stay with Ross.'

'That was just a dream of mine, dear,' Cynthia assured her daughter hastily. 'I've learnt through long experience that none of my dreams come true.'

Thus speaks the wife of my father, Suzanne thought sadly. My father, who crushes underfoot everybody's dreams as a way of attaining his own.

Cynthia persisted, as though the subject was now worrying her, 'You do still want to divorce him, don't you, dear?'

Suzanne's shoulders lifted and drooped. 'All I can say, Mother, is that I've got an appointment to see the solicitor tomorrow.'

Cynthia nodded without speaking. There was a ring at the door, and Suzanne frowned, wondering who would know she was at home. Opening the door, she noted that another small car was parked beside her mother's. The woman who stood on the doorstep was smiling brightly.

'I'm Mrs Hadley,' she told Suzanne. 'Your husband suggested I might call this morning since you were having a day off work. I expect he told you?'

Suzanne mentally ground her teeth. Her husband had not told her! She opened the door wide and the woman came in. Her movements were brisk, her manner confident. Suzanne had already decided that this was the housekeeper she would have chosen from a dozen others.

An introduction to her mother was made and they chatted for a few moments. How much had Ross told the woman about their future plans? It seemed from her conversation that she knew nothing of any forthcoming divorce.

'Three times a week, I think,' Suzanne estimated. 'There are only two of us and we're both out at work until evening.'

Mrs Hadley frowned. 'Your husband told me I'd be needed every day, except weekends, ten until five. I thought you must have discussed it.'

'Oh—oh, yes, of course,' Suzanne bluffed. 'I remember now. We couldn't make up our minds at first. Well,' she rose and Mrs Hadley followed, turning to say goodbye to Mrs Cannon, 'shall we say the day after tomorrow? I expect you discussed your salary with my husband?' Mrs Hadley was not to know that the sweetness of Suzanne's smile was adulterated with bitterness at Ross's failure to consult her.

Mrs Hadley confirmed that she had indeed agreed a weekly wage with Mr Beckett and that she looked forward to working for Mrs Beckett as from the day after tomorrow.

Suzanne found her mother in the kitchen washing the dishes. 'How thoughtful of Ross to arrange for you to have a housekeeper! If you were intending to stay with him, you wouldn't need to have a job . . .'

Her mother, Suzanne decided, was talking to herself, drifting off on one of her unobtainable dreams. At the door, her mother's embrace was clinging, heartbreakingly so. Her instinctive feeling that her mother had all those years ago needed her support might not have been far wrong, after all.

'Come and see me sometimes, dear,' Cynthia pleaded, 'whether your father's at home or not. I know you two don't get on, but,' with intensity her eyes held those of her daughter, 'I think I can guess what kind of a sacrifice you're making on his—on our company's behalf.'

Eyes moistening at her mother's unexpected insight, Suzanne hugged her mother back. 'As long as you're all right, Mum—that's all that matters to me now.' If her mother heard the note of utter despondency, she couldn't help it, since that was how she felt about the whole situation.

Watching her mother's car speed away down the drive, Suzanne found her thoughts dwelling on the reason for her unhappiness. Tomorrow she would be taking the first step towards breaking away for ever from Ross. Everything in her rebelled against it, but something drove her on. What that 'something' was she could not discover, no matter how hard she tried.

Early that afternoon, the removal firm employed by Maggie to deliver customers' goods drew up in the driveway. There was a hammering on the door and the men on the doorstep recognised Suzanne. They grinned, making some comment about the best way of making a profit in your own shop was to buy the goods yourself.

Cheerfully, they carried in the small amount of furniture, both upstairs and down, even arranging the patio chairs and table for her. When she offered them an extra large tip, they pretended to wave it away, then grabbed the money before it went out of their reach. Then, still laughing and joking, they left.

For the remainder of the afternoon, the sense of goodwill the men had left behind stayed with Suzanne. Later, going into the kitchen, she wondered what kind of dish to cook for herself and Ross that evening. Once again, she did not know if he would be home. In the end, she took a calculated risk and decided to cook a meal for two.

Ross stayed out late. Nearly three hours after Suzanne had cooked the meal, she threw away his portion. She felt angry with herself for preparing it and even more angry with him for treating her so callously. All he'd needed to do was to pick up a phone and call her.

Unable to settle to anything, she had a shower. It was still too early to go to bed, knowing also that she would not rest until she heard Ross come in. Finding fresh clothes, she dressed, then wondered again what to do. After a glance at the dividing door between the main building and the extension, the fancy took her to go exploring again.

With Ross away from the house, it was an ideal time, she decided, to look at that self-contained suite of rooms. The same good taste as she had discerned in the rest of the furnishings prevailed here, too. For whom was the place intended? Maybe he meant it for his mother who, he had said in passing, was currently staying with friends in Brittany.

Moving out of the apartment and along the corridor, she went into the room which Ross had referred to as her own special work-room. There were other pieces of furniture she would need ... Hurriedly, she quenched the flames of her mounting excitement.

In a few months, she wouldn't be here, so why was she so foolishly planning her future needs? The tension of anticipation left her and she felt empty and drained, like a cave that had been filled and deserted by a flowing tide.

That emptiness was with her when she wandered into the room next door, which Ross had called the nursery. Here, there were four walls, nothing more. But her imagination flooded the tall echoing area with sounds of laughter and squabbling children, of noisy toys and the fresh-cheeked breathing of afternoon sleepers.

*The children would not be hers!* She covered her face, felt her body tremble at the thought that it would never be allowed to carry the growing new life which she and Ross might, in happier circumstances, have implanted there, the result of their joyous coming-together through their love for each other.

Hands descending on to her shoulders shocked her into stillness. He was home, standing in front of her, his face in shadow. 'Crying for the moon? For what might have been?' he asked. Unable to speak for the tears which ran downwards unheeding of her efforts to check them, Suzanne shook herself free. 'Whenever you regret the past,' Ross persisted cruelly, 'remember that you were the one who broke up our marriage.'

Her distressed eyes stared up at him. '*You* walked out on me. If you'd stayed, I'd still be truly your wife. We'd have had a couple of children, by now, maybe three.'

'You'd have made me a fine marriage partner, wouldn't you, blocking my career prospects right from the start.' His sneering attitude maddened her like the sting of a clump of nettles. All the same, her honesty told her he hadn't really been in the wrong.

He had worked so hard, against such difficulties, for his degree. Night after night, in the room they had shared, she had watched his bent head lovingly and proudly as he wrote pages of notes, read highly technical books. Whenever he had gone away on field trips, she had waited with unending patience for his return.

Whichever way you looked at it, she argued, he was not completely blameless. 'You could have written,' she accused. 'You must have had leave. You could have flown home to see me to reason things out.'

His cool stare made her shiver. There was no way of reaching him. Yet his evening outfit increased that magnetism of which he possessed so much. Its very formality conversely emphasised the easy confidence of his manner, and reminded her embarrassingly of her own carelessness of dress.

It also added to his air of remoteness, adding another layer to the glacial barrier that divided them. She would break through his icy politeness, she resolved, she would cross that frozen barrier, no matter how much effort it required.

'I suppose you've been dining with your "woman friend",' she challenged, forcing down her underlying misery at the thought. 'With your female geologist companion who worked by your side while you were abroad? Maybe,' she gestured wildly, 'you've got it planned for her to bear your children and fill this room with their—their laughter, their——'

She had goaded him to whip his hands from his pockets and grip her round the waist. She winced at the pinching pain, but he merely tightened his hold. His eyes blazed with cold heat, glittering like alpine snows in the deceptively golden sunshine.

His lips were a straight line, his jaw hard with resolve. 'You want to bear my children? There's only one way to achieve that, my precious, and that is for me to take you to my bed. We'll indulge in some of that "conjugal bliss" you dismissed so casually yesterday.'

He swept her up and carried her. 'No,' she screamed, 'I'm not sleeping with you! You can't force me. You——'

They were outside his bedroom. He kicked open the door and stood her down, turning the key and planting himself, legs apart, in front of it.

'Now undress.'

She did not obey, but watched as he removed his jacket and released his bow tie.

'We'd live separately,' she said hoarsely. 'You said you wanted me back, to live with you. Well, I'm fulfilling the condition. I'm living with you. You can't—you just can't renege on your promise.'

Now his shirt was gone, flying in an arc to hit a chair. He looked her up and down as though she was already naked, and her arms went round her own shivering body as if she had already complied with his order.

'I made no promise,' he responded curtly, 'either to you or your father. Live with me, I said, and that covers a lot—a hell of a lot of things. I'm going to shower. By the time I get back, I'll expect you to be in my bed, ready for me. Do you get that?'

There was no reply she could make. Already she was planning to escape while he was out of the room. Her plans were in vain, since he appeared to have a bathroom of his own, through a door leading off the large bedroom. The key was still in his possession as he went to shower.

When he returned a few minutes later, he was wearing only a robe. He found her seated on the bed, huddled up, all her muscles tensed. Even her jaw was clamped so as to shut out any kisses he might try to take.

'I said get undressed.' His words came softly, dangerously.

'Suzanne's brown eyes lifted, large with fear, yet still defiant. 'You'll have to half kill me to get me to take these things off!'

Slowly, his bare feet brought him nearer. 'I'll give you one more chance.'

Her muscles were growing tired with tension, yet she spat, 'You can *have* your chance.' Then she held her breath for the onslaught.

It did not come. Instead, she saw him removing his robe, first untying the belt, opening it wide, slipping it from his shoulders, throwing it from him. Fascinated, she stared. It seemed that not only inwardly had he changed.

His body had matured into an unimagined toughness, developing a strength which beckoned her to come, yet which dared her to do so. It still bore the tan, only slightly fading, which his skin had acquired after years spent under the African sun.

This was her husband—yes, he was that still. No step had yet been taken to part them asunder. One thing she knew as she relaxed her limbs—she needed him, wanted him, *loved him*. No other man would ever take his place, even when she had been divorced from him for a lifetime.

A lifetime without him! The terrible, lonely years stretched into infinity. One night of loving him, a whisper said—a long and final night with the man she loved, how could that be wrong?

'Touch me, touch me.' She heard the urgency in his words and found herself responding. Like a sleepwalker, her hand came out in front of her, groping for him, touching his hip, finding the leanness of his waist. Her eyes ensnared by his, she discovered that her legs were supporting her.

'Remember, remember.' His voice was an invisible guide in the strange darkness in which she was wandering. I remember, she whispered to herself, how we made love, unworried, unhurried, despite other people's noises all around us, outside the locked door.

His chest . . . her fingertips trailed through the dark mass, up to shoulder, neck and chin. Lips were moving under her touch, kissing each finger. Then his arms were holding her and she felt the rough brush of his skin against hers, felt his hand on her thrusting breasts, teasing the hardening points.

She tried to look down, but Ross's fist beneath her chin would not allow it. All the time she had been re-discovering paths over the relief map of his body, he had been undressing her. Now they stood together, naked together.

He pushed her backwards on to the bed, swinging her round, pinning her down. There was a hand behind her lower back, urging her closer, making her feel his need. Like a flower opening to the sun, she opened her very being to him, crying out with joy at his possession, ec-static in her abandonment to him of her body.

They lay, locked together, for an endless time, his breath caressing her cheek, his mouth, still now, against her throat. Rolling away, he reached for the cover which had slipped to the floor, he tugged it up and over them, slipping his arms around her again.

'Sleep now,' he said softly and, still under his spell, her eyes fluttered closed and she slept.

In the night, or was it in her dream, she felt him caressing her. Her skin was electric under his slow, inti-mate touches. His mouth followed his hands' path and her entire body sang a rapturous song. Impatient now, he came back to her, taking her again, more possessive than ever before. Above the golden cloud, the sun shone, dazzling and showing a glimpse of total joy.

I'm his, he's mine! Even as they separated from one another a long time afterwards, and lay entwined, the words kept on, leading her thoughts into a future where nothing would ever part them again.

Awakening to daylight, she felt for him. His side of the bed was empty. For a while, she lay curled up and contented. It had had to happen, she knew that. He had not forced her, nor had it been sacrifice on her part.

It had, she supposed, been inevitable, that turning back of time—for once to the year of happiness, instead of the succeeding and empty years.

The tick of an alarm clock told her that such a thing as time existed and there was no way whatsoever of turning it back. Eight-thirty, and her appointment with the solicitor was in just one hour's time.

She dived out of bed, then stopped. How could she part from Ross when she loved him so much? When only last night they had renewed their marriage and restated their love . . .

Sinking back on to the bed, Suzanne closed her eyes, remembering how, time after time, she had murmured, I love you. And he had kissed her more passionately with each fresh avowal of her love for him. Now she had lain in his arms again and once more known and exulted in the thrusting intimacy of his lovemaking, there was no way in which she could suffer the agony of a final parting. Nothing, she decided, would make her go through with the divorce.

It was only as she dried herself after a shower that she remembered this was the day the housekeeper would be starting her job.

Dressing so fast, she was breathless, she raced across to the extension telephone in Ross's bedroom and cancelled her appointment with the solicitor. Standing afterwards, hand to her head, she felt the tension drain from her. The decision had been made and acted upon. Now she would have to face the consequences.

# CHAPTER EIGHT

IT did not take long to ease Mrs Hadley into the pattern of the work she would be expected to do each morning. Suzanne told her to make her own choice of tasks from the mental list she had in her head.

With her experience, Suzanne commented, and knowing the house from the past, she felt she could safely leave the various jobs to the housekeeper's own common sense. Mrs Hadley said she was pleased to know that Mrs Beckett had so much trust in her and promised to keep the house spotless, even doing some shopping if Mrs Beckett would be so good as to leave a list now and then.

Feeling that a load had been lifted from her shoulders, Suzanne entered the shop to find Maggie grinning and waving a cheque. The amount of money it represented made Suzanne gasp.

'Is that how much Ross has paid for the shop?' she asked.

Maggie nodded. 'Plus its contents, goodwill and so on. I just couldn't go and pay it into my bank account until I'd shown it to you.'

'If I were you,' Suzanne advised, 'I'd get it to the bank as quickly as my legs would take me.'

'Tell me something,' Maggie said at the door, 'just why did your husband act the knight in shining armour towards me in my trouble?'

'Haven't the slightest idea, Maggie, honestly.'

Maggie allowed herself a small, accusing frown. 'You wouldn't have had anything to do with it, would you?'

'I swear I didn't, apart from telling him.'

'Ah.' Maggie tapped her chin thoughtfully with the envelope which contained the cheque. 'Oh well, mine is not to reason why, to misquote the well-known saying, mine is but to go and pay it in and rejoice in my good fortune.'

Putting the envelope lovingly to her lips, she went out and ran all the way along the road to the bank.

Suzanne sat at the table behind the screen. In a pile, there were printed, scarlet notices announcing a sale. Ross must have instructed Maggie to hold it, she reasoned, since he was now the shop's owner.

Maggie had asked her why Ross had acted so bountifully towards her. For whom had he really taken such a step—for Maggie, himself, or——? It couldn't be for me, she whispered. Could it? Ruefully, she shook her head. There was no possible reason why he should have had her in mind, and every possible reason against it.

Maggie returned, waving a bottle. Hearing the door opening, Suzanne had peeped round the screen. 'No customers?' Maggie asked, looking round surreptitiously. 'Good. We can toast—well, everything. The shop, your husband, me, you——' She stopped short.

'Suzanne, I'm sorry!' Her grey eyes widened. Putting the bottle of champagne on the table, she pushed her brown hair behind her ears. 'I forgot your appointment with the solicitor. What happened? Do you want to cry on my shoulder, or chortle with relief?'

Suzanne laughed. 'It's okay. I didn't go, Maggie. I cancelled the appointment.'

'Am I allowed to poke my nose in and ask why? Ah, I can see by your smile that I'm not. And don't think I shall let my imagination run riot, imagining reconciliations and—and everything. But it means, I hope, we can drink to the future—all our futures.'

'I'll find a couple of glasses.' Suzanne raked in a cupboard. 'Will these do?' She held up two tumblers. 'It's all I can find.'

Maggie nodded and grinned. 'You don't think I'm going to fill them, do you? I mean, I want some left to take home so that Dan and I can drink to the future, too.'

They were draining their glasses when the door bell

rang. 'Customer,' Maggie whispered. 'I'll go.' She made to emerge from the screen, then stopped. 'Hey, who's in charge here now? Me—or you? I mean, it was your husband who——'

'You, definitely, Maggie. He said I could work here for as long——' She stopped quickly. She could not tell her friend the cruel answer which Ross had given to her question, no matter how much she wanted to. 'He just said I could go on working here,' she finished, hoping Maggie wouldn't probe.

Maggie nodded, put a finger to her lips and automatically adopted her caring-shop-assistant act.

Mrs Hadley had left the house so tidy and neat that it was, to Suzanne, a pleasure to walk in that evening. There was a faint smell of lingering polish, everything shone, and even the piles of magazines and newspapers had been neatened. A bowl of fragrant flowers from the garden stood on the hall table.

Having eaten—this time she had cooked only for one—and cleared away, Suzanne stretched into relaxation. For the first time for years—since Ross had walked out on her—life felt good.

When the telephone rang, her heart jumped and she ran to answer the call. It must be Ross, she reasoned, to tell her when she could expect him home. It was Miles, and Suzanne had difficulty in keeping the disappointment out of her voice.

'What did the solicitor say, Suzanne?' he asked anxiously. Strange, she thought idly, how his questions about the progress of the divorce proceedings were always so much more eager than his lovemaking.

'I didn't go. I mean,' she hastened to add, thinking quickly of a white lie, 'he—he was called away unexpectedly.' She crossed her fingers, hoping her evasion would be accepted.

'Well, did you make another appointment?' She resented the irritation with which he asked the question.

'I will—in a few days. When he's back,' she added swiftly, to block any further interrogation.

'Can I see you tonight, Suzanne?' She made a negative sound. 'Why not?' he pressed. 'Your husband can't insist on your staying at home every night, or any night, come to that. You shouldn't really be there at all, in view of the fact that you're going to divorce him.'

Gently she soothed him, telling him she would call him back in a day or two. Partially pacified, he rang off. It was then that the hours seemed to crawl. Switching on the television, Suzanne relaxed on the couch. Determinedly she kept her mind on the programme, but after a while the determination weakened.

Her thoughts would keep drifting back to the night she had spent in Ross's arms. The feeling of being whole again, a complete person, was too pleasurable to be put aside in favour of watching real people pretending to be unreal people in a television play set in a space capsule which had plunged into some unspecified time in the future.

Her future was now, here, with her, and her present and her past. They had all joined within her last night in the act of reunion with her husband.

Switching off the television set, she went slowly up to bed. It was so late now that she knew Ross must have eaten out, but she had not given up all hope of seeing him. She would wash and prepare for bed, then read until he returned.

When the entrance door opened, she was alert at once. The sound of his footsteps on the stairs operated an on-switch in her body, speeding up the blood-flow and raising her emotional thermostat.

The footsteps paused outside and her fingers gripped the closed book she held. Would he come in? They moved on and she heard him go into his bedroom. The book fell to the bed. With her head resting back, she listened to the tread of his feet around the room.

Pushing the bedclothes aside, she made for the door, snatching a robe from a hook and pulling it on. If she could catch him before he disappeared into his bathroom, she would tell him about her decision.

Standing in his doorway, she realised he was already there. She could hear the sound of rushing water, which meant he was taking a shower. Should she wait? she wondered. Had she the courage—but he was her husband, so what need was there for courage? Boldly, she walked across to sit on his bed. Running a hand lightly over the cover, she told herself that, after last night, it was her bed, too.

Ross must have sensed her presence, since he emerged from the adjoining bathroom, a towel tied round his waist. His wet hair was ruffled with drying, his hands spread over his towel-covered hips, the twin columns of his legs placed firmly apart.

His chest hair was in whorls which were pressed flat to his body. The muscles in his upper arms stood out, telling of their latent strength. Suzanne found it was as much as she could do to resist the magnetism of him, remembering the hard, male feel of his body against hers in the night.

Her smile was uncertain yet winsome, unconsciously so, as she gazed back. He let his eyes wander the length and breadth of her, then her smile faded as she realised that she hadn't even begun to touch his heart.

'Well, have you set things going?' he asked. 'Do I now have a case to defend?'

'I didn't go. I cancelled the appointment.'

There was a long silence, then he asked, 'Don't you mean postponed?'

'Cancelled,' she answered, and wondered if he had heard the whisper.

'I suppose I'm allowed to ask why?' He seemed so distant she began to despair. Then his eyes narrowed. 'No, don't tell me. It was because of last night. Right?'

Suzanne nodded, half-turning. 'I—I'll go. I only came to tell you, and to say——' she moistened her lips with the tip of her tongue, and gave a tentative smile, 'to say "Hallo, again" like we used to.' He did not move. Her brown eyes dropped under his intense gaze. 'I'll go.' She turned away, but he was there, holding her wrist, pulling her inside and closing the door.

Bunching his hand, he lifted her chin. The planes of his face were hard in the soft illumination from the bedside lamp. A half-smile played over his lips. 'I see . . . a question, an invitation.'

The vigorous shaking of her head was mere lip-service to the convention of 'man must chase woman'. By the gleam in his eyes, Ross knew it. Her lips grew soft and tremulous as she tried to tell him, without words, I love you.

With an impatient tug, he released the towel around him and it fell to the floor. 'By God,' he said softly, 'I can't resist the woman in you. I never could.'

One hand found the small of her back, urging her nearer, while the other eased the robe away from her until it, too, found the floor. The transparent nightgown veiled every feminine feature of her in a pink haze and as he tugged her against him, she felt the warm throb of his maleness through the thin fabric.

'I want you,' he said, his mouth moving again over her throat, 'and I'm going to take you. But first, this must go.' He slid the ribbon straps of the nightdress from her shoulders, one by one. The rest of it slithered to her waist, past her hips to join the other discarded items.

He lifted her and let his eyes make a lazy, sensual inventory of her naked body. The sensation of his muscled arms supporting her, his bare skin exciting hers, made it tingle as if electrically charged, rekindling every slumbering desire within her. In that first and only real year of marriage, she could not recall this intensity of feeling, this craving to be one with him.

They must have been there, she thought feverishly as he put her full length on his bed, immediately joining her. Except that now she was older, her body was more mature, its response mechanism more finely-balanced and receptive. Slowly, seductively Ross touched her, trailing his fingers the length of her, then moving upward again. Holding her eyes, he circled her breasts, watching the colour flood her face, the brown of her eyes deepen with longing.

Then his lips and teeth teased the pink peaks until her

breath came sharply, then from the depths of her as her pleasure mounted. His hands were seeking with familiarity and expertise the intimate softness of her, waiting until her hands grasped his hair and she cried out, 'Love me, darling, love me!'

A long time later, they still lay entwined, satiated and slowly descending from the high plateau of shared ecstasy. I've come home, Suzanne thought hazily and smiling, I've come home to Ross's arms.

In the morning, she awoke to find him leaning over her. He smelt clean and fresh and was fully dressed. For a moment, she was over-conscious of her unclothed state, but the embarrassment passed quickly. What did it matter how little she wore now they were so much a part of each other?

His finger traced a line down her profile, along her nose, over the full lips, to rest on her rounded chin. It did not stop there. Her smile was dazzling as she felt the finger wander farther down to invade the valley which divided her breasts. When it passed over her stomach, still making its determined way onward, she squealed and seized his hand, laughing up at him.

His smile caught at hers and intertwined. His mouth came homing and parted her lips, invading until her arms reached up to cling.

Finally he straightened. His gaze dwelt thoughtfully upon her face. At last, he covered her with the quilt, bent to brush her lips with his and left her alone.

Suzanne telephoned her mother from the shop. Maggie was not there to hear the conversation. She had gone places, as she had put it, looking for new items to stock.

Her mother was delighted to hear from her. 'Won't you come over some time?' Cynthia asked, a little wistfully. 'I miss you, dear. I used to love our heart-to-hearts.' She laughed reminiscently. 'You know, when you told me your thoughts about things and I told you mine. It helped me solve my—little problems.'

The only problem you have, Suzanne thought but

could not say, is one rather rounded, too well-built man, with opinions that swamp everyone else's, especially yours.

'Well,' she said aloud, 'I was thinking of coming to see you later today. What time is Father home from work?'

'A little earlier these days, dear. He brings the account books home. It's getting more and more difficult to balance them.' She gave a small, bewildered laugh. 'Things are getting more difficult for him, too.'

'Even after Ross's loan?'

'Even after that, dear. Your father does tell me, but I don't understand the technicalities of high finance. He was talking of trying to find another source of cash. I just don't know.'

Suzanne felt stricken, but she had to see her father. Events could not be allowed to drift, unresolved, now that she had made up her mind.

'Would he be in around four o'clock?' she asked.

'Make it a little after that, dear.'

'I will. 'Bye, Mum, for now.'

Maggie arrived mid-afternoon, announcing she had made a few finds deep in the countryside. 'Amazing,' she commented, 'how many intriguing craft workshops are springing up, in cottages, sheds, barns, almost any old building with a roof and four walls. The people who run them are always delighted to hear of a new outlet.'

'I think it's wonderful,' Suzanne answered. 'Seems like we're slowly going back in time to when people produced everything with their hands.'

'Don't forget brains,' added Maggie, tapping her head. 'Not that there's much in mine.' She grinned. 'Want to know why I'm happy? Tonight, Dan and I are making it official. He's giving me an engagement ring, and some time, we'll fix the date.'

Suzanne's hands came together with delight. 'That's great! Just as long as he's not the old-fashioned kind who won't let his wife go out to work!'

'Oh, no. If Maggie says she's staying in her job,'

Maggie said, 'Maggie stays in her job. Incidentally, Dan was delighted to know the weight of running this place had been taken off my shoulders by your wonderful husband.'

To Suzanne's annoyance, her cheeks grew hot. Maggie did not comment, merely laughed. 'By the way,' she added, 'didn't you tell me yesterday you might want to leave early this afternoon?'

'To see my mother—well, really my father.' Maggie nodded and asked her, Well, why didn't she go? Suzanne was glad that her friend did not ask questions.

Her mother embraced her when she arrived. 'I've made some tea. You will have a cup, won't you?'

'Don't treat me like a guest, Mum, in my own home,' Suzanne protested, accepting a cup from her mother. It was, she noted, the best tea service.

Cynthia laughed, but Suzanne thought she could detect a certain strain. 'Is it still your home, dear, now you're back with Ross?'

'Back with Ross?' Suzanne smiled. 'That sounds very permanent, Mother. I—don't know whether—I'm going to continue living with him, do I?'

'I rather got the impression, dear, that you liked being there.'

Suzanne was saved the difficulty of finding an answer when her father erupted into the house. 'What's that girl's car doing outside?' he shouted from the entrance hall. 'If she's come here with her——'

'Hallo, Father.' Suzanne was smiling up at him, mouth faintly curved, youthful brown eyes striking sparks off older brown eyes.

Lucas looked around, head thrust forward with suspicion, 'Is *he* with you?'

'If by "he" you mean Ross, he's in London, at his place of work.'

'You trying to put me in my place, girl?'

Cynthia, foreseeing trouble, intervened to soothe. 'She's come to see us, dear. Isn't that nice? You know she's always welcome in her own home.'

'Is she?' He walked across to his desk in the corner. Were his legs feeling as heavy to him as they looked? Suzanne wondered, frowning. 'If this is her home, then why did you bother to get out the best china?'

'You've made your point, Father. I know you can't wait to get rid of me——' She paused as her mother made a faint sound of protest. 'But I had to come. I'm honest, you see.'

He swung in his chair. 'You, honest?'

'Honest! Like you, Father. I told you I had a lot of you in me, didn't I?'

He looked at his daughter suspiciously. 'Are you trying to get on the right side of me, with your devious ways?'

'If I'm devious,' she took him up, triumph flaring, 'then it must have come from——'

His fist hit the fragile bureau, shaking it. 'To hell with your word-twisting! What do you want?'

'To tell you I've changed my mind about divorcing Ross.'

It seemed to take a few moments for the information to register. Then his swivel chair swung slowly. 'You've what?'

Suzanne repeated her statement, flinching at the vicious look in his eyes, but showing none of it.

'Does he know about his good fortune?' her father questioned with heavy sarcasm.

Her eyes dropped away, falsely demure, then lifted to blaze into his. 'Not in so many words. There are other ways of—of communicating with one's husband or wife. Or had you forgotten?'

'I won't stand for your impudence!' Lucas came heavily across the room. Cynthia's hand went protectively out towards her daughter. Suzanne did not move. She would have taken whatever might have been coming, anyway. Nothing did, for the simple reason that Lucas had just absorbed into his brain the meaning of his daughter's decision.

'No divorce, you say?' He sat in a chair. 'Do you

realise what effect this momentous decision of yours is going to have on my business? It's going to make me bankrupt,' he thumped the cushioned arm, 'that's what it's going to do!'

'I'm sorry about that, Father.' Her cheeks had paled but her eyes did battle. 'I tried to help you by putting your interests first and going back to live with Ross. I thought it would be only temporary, too. I wasn't to know, was I, that I'd fall in love with him all over again?' Not that I ever stopped, she thought.

'The basis of that condition was that you'd live separate lives. He took good care to see that that part of the deal was broken, didn't he? Clever, too, when you think about it. Make love to a woman and she clings. That's how it goes in life, and my God, he knew it!'

Lucas hoisted himself up. 'I'm going to see Bill Harringdon. I'm putting my cards on the table. He's an old friend, he'll understand. I'll tell him the marriage between you and his son will have to be postponed.'

'But, Father, it won't take place.'

Her father repeated, each word distinct, 'The marriage will be postponed.' At his desk, he reached for the telephone extension, saying over his shoulder, 'There will be a divorce, then you'll marry Bill's son.' He dialled, tapping with his fingernails.

Suzanne and her mother exchanged glances. Cynthia indicated to Suzanne that she should help herself to another cup of tea. Suzanne noticed that her mother's hand was trembling.

'Miss Rutledge?' Lucas was speaking now. 'Is Bill Harringdon available? It's Lucas Cannon. I'd like to speak to him. He's out? An important appointment in London? When's he due back? Around midnight, if then? Yes, it's urgent. Call again in the morning?' Lucas's tone had sharpened. 'It's urgent, I tell you. What? Do I expect you to bring him back on a magic carpet? Do you know who you're talking to?'

He crashed down the receiver, swinging to unload his ire on to his daughter.

'It'll be all right when I've seen Bill Harringdon. Then you'll stay with that upstart over my dead body, do you hear? He only took you back temporarily, to spite me. He married you to spite me, to get even with me for holding back parental permission to marry you. Yes,' he sneered, 'I can see you haven't thought about it that way, have you?'

Suzanne stared expressionlessly back at her father. New anxieties had sprung, like weeds appearing overnight in a garden, needling worries planted there by his words.

Standing, she challenged back, old ways taking over, the habit of years rekindling defiance. 'I'm staying married to Ross, no matter what you say, until—if and when it ever comes—the day he decides he made a mistake seven years ago and wants to marry someone else.'

'I'm glad you realise you might not be the only woman in his life. He's a man—anyone can see that by looking—so six years without a woman would be asking too much. I can see you haven't thought about that, either.' He rubbed his hands. 'I'll get my way. I'll get you away from him yet.'

'You're getting nowhere, Father,' Suzanne countered. 'I know how he feels about me.'

Lucas's smile was unpleasant. 'A man can feel that way about more than one woman, many more.' With that final shot, he stomped from the room.

Arriving home, Suzanne was haunted by a feeling of failure. When her father had stormed at her, she had remained apparently cool and composed, but she had wanted to cover her ears to shut out his accusations.

Hanging up her jacket, she dropped into an armchair and closed her eyes. Had she committed such a terrible crime by falling in love, second time round, with her husband? It appeared that this was how her father viewed the matter.

The sound of soft-walking footsteps made her eyes open wide. Ross stood watching her, expression enigmatic, glass in hand. His eyebrows lifted and he offered her his glass. Her gaze moved to fix on it and she did not shake her head.

He moved round to stand in front of her and she sat up, taking the glass and swallowing a drink or two. It was stronger than her usual choice and she made a face. If she had drunk from his side, she did not care. There was the feel of his legs against her knees as he bent, smiling, to take back the drink.

'Rough day?' he asked.

Should she tell him where she had been? It would not, in the circumstances, be advisable. Her shoulders lifted noncommittally. 'Maybe.'

The shadow of a frown passed across his forehead, but he made no comment, and Suzanne's fingers tightened on the arms of the chair. The meal—she should be the one to prepare and cook it, shouldn't she? Even if her appetite was shrinking by the minute, Ross would be in need of food.

Facing him, she said, 'I'm sorry. I almost forgot— what would you like to eat? Unless you're going out?'

'I'm eating out.' Suzanne forced herself to nod understandingly. He had not changed from his working suit, despite the fact that he seemed to have taken a shower. The damp still lingered on his thick hair, and her fingers itched to push it back from his eyes.

'Oh. Well, I'll go and search for something for myself.'

'You're eating out, too. With me.'

'You mean——' She frowned. 'Ah, I understand. Your date's let you down and you booked a table for two.' She knew her smile was strained. 'In that case——'

'You're my date, Suzanne.'

Her whole expression lightened. 'Are you sure?'

He picked up her left hand and looked with meaning at the wedding ring he had given her. With an eyebrow raised, he commented, 'Need I say more?'

Pleasure flooded through her and she shook her head.

'Is there time for me to have a quick shower and change?'

'Plenty.'

At the door, she paused. 'Thanks, Ross.'

His hands were in his pockets as he responded, 'Shouldn't I be thanking you?'

'Me? For what?' Her brows pleated, then it came to her. 'Oh, you mean for—that.' Momentarily, the sparkle went out of the day. What she had done had not been for gain. She loved him, didn't he understand, hadn't she told him often enough last night?

There was no more to say on the subject. 'I'll get ready.' Even she could hear how flat her voice had gone.

The dress she chose was daffodil yellow and silky, with long sleeves and a throat-hugging neckline. The narrow frill at the waist echoed those at the cuffs. The gold, hooped earrings and long gold pendant had been gifts from her father.

It was these that caught Ross's eyes as she entered. Walking to face him, she smiled up at him, seeking for his approval. Instead, he was frowning. His finger flicked the earrings, while his hand followed the plunge of the pendant downward to the inset garnet at its end.

'Which past boy-friend gave you these?' His tone scratched, while the back of his hand rested familiarly against her breasts.

'No boy-friend. My father.' She could see he did not believe her. 'He showered my mother with jewellery, too. He gave it to me instead of love.'

He studied her face as if to discover how sincere she was in making such a devastatingly frank statement. 'And yet you opted to stay with him—with them both—instead of coming with me?'

'For my mother's sake.'

'As you keep saying. Come on.' His hand caught her arm, then he stopped, bent down and inhaled just beneath her ear. 'Enticing. Are you out to seduce me again?'

Suzanne frowned. 'Again?' Was he saying that the two nights they had made love had been initiated by her?

Ross must have felt her sudden stiffness, since he tugged impatiently, giving her her coat.

In the car, she asked, 'Where are we going?'

'To a restaurant I know. It's a few miles from here.'

Suzanne gazed out at the benign summer evening. The country lane was, as usual, narrow, following the route laid down for it probably many centuries earlier. Ross turned the car into a long drive, slowing his speed as he drove carefully over a narrow road leading to a large house.

'It looks very grand,' Suzanne commented.

'The welcome is warm.'

'Have you been here often?'

He lifted a shoulder and dropped it. He was plainly disinclined to tell her anything about his separate life. It was a pity, she reflected not without envy, she had no 'separate life' to match his.

'It's an old manor house,' he volunteered as he braked in the nearby car park. 'Open as a restaurant from spring to autumn.'

The welcome was indeed warm—for Ross. The head waiter greeted him as an old friend. 'It's good to see you again, sir. And your lady.' He bowed. 'You'd like a secluded table again, sir?'

'Very,' was the dry reply.

The head waiter smiled. 'The lady who is usually with you seems to like it, sir, so I naturally assumed——?'

'This is my wife,' Ross cut him off sharply.

'Ah,' the man smoothly covered his gaffe, 'it's good to take one's wife out to dinner.' He was leading the way to a table. 'It adds to the romance of love.' Even as he was speaking, his mind was on his job. I wonder, Suzanne reflected wryly, if he really knows what he's saying.

He did not linger, having seen another couple appear at the entrance. Ross looked round. The wine waiter was already on his way. Ross ordered aperitifs, then said to Suzanne,

'All right, ask me the identity of the woman I bring here.'

I won't let him know he's hurting me, Suzanne vowed. 'I don't want to know. I wouldn't dream of asking, just as I hope you wouldn't probe if you discovered there was another man in my life.'

Ross's eyes cooled down. The aperitifs were served and Suzanne stared at hers with concentration. 'I assumed there already was,' Ross answered. 'One Harringdon, Miles?'

'Yes, of course.' She hoped he did not notice her lack of enthusiasm.

Ross drank and she copied him, her eyes watching as his hand went to his jacket pocket. He brought out a small box and eased open the lid. It held a diamond and gold ring, fashioned in an intricate modern setting.

He leaned across the table, holding out the box. 'I thought it was about time I gave you an engagement ring. Do you like it? I had it made especially for you.'

Her eyes were shining like the two diamonds. 'But, Ross, it must have cost a lot of money!'

'When we married, I wanted to buy you one, but I couldn't afford it. We're not poor any more, Suzanne,' he added.

His use of the plural gave her even more pleasure than the gift of the ring.

'I like it, Ross, I like it so much. May I——?'

'No. That's my privilege.' He pushed it into place, then lifted her hand to his lips. She wanted to throw her arms round his neck. 'Seven years is a long time to wait.'

She replied, her eyes on the ring, 'A long time to wait also for one's husband to return.'

He did not answer, and she was forced to look at him. Her glance caught the end of a look of total seriousness. His features softened into a smile. 'I hope you don't think I gave you that piece of jewellery instead of love.'

She laughed, remembering her comment earlier about her father's gifts. 'The thought hadn't occurred to me,' earnestly she sought his eyes, 'until now.'

The menu was placed in their hands and her view of his face was blocked.

Through the meal the conversation was on neutral subjects. Ross talked about his experiences in Nigeria, both amusing and serious. He talked about the heat and the hard work. Not once did he mention his friend and co-geologist, Tania Marlowe.

How much did she mean to him? Suzanne agonised. When he had first talked about her, he'd referred to her as in the present, not the past. I have a woman friend, he had said. Where was she now?

It was getting late when they arrived home, but not late enough, it seemed, for Ross to want to go to bed. He threw aside his jacket and offered Suzanne a drink, but she refused, smiling up at him. He did not smile back. He took one for himself, switching on the television set as he passed. He sat beside her on the couch, loosening his tie, stretching his legs, his eyes on the chat show on the screen.

Suzanne tried to fix her attention on it, too, but Ross's nearness was making her agitated. Her hand wanted to stray across to him, so she clasped it with the other hand. Instead, she touched him with her eyes, certain that he was too absorbed to notice.

The toughness of his thighs was outlined by the close fit of his trousers, the leanness around his waist emphasised by the narrow leather belt. Suzanne wanted to rest her tired head against the solidity of his chest ... Slowly his head turned and he was watching her watching him. His eyebrows lifted in a question. He was remote again and a stranger, not the man she had married. Where had he gone?

Colour dyed her cheeks and she stood up quickly. 'Goodnight, Ross.'

He got to his feet and she wanted to shout, Don't be so polite. For the last two nights, we've slept together. You're my husband, remember? I'm not a guest.

At the door, she turned. 'I'm sorry, Ross, but I forgot to thank you for——' she held out her hand, 'for this beautiful ring.'

Just before she shut the door, he called out, 'You still haven't thanked me—properly.'

He's not going to catch me that way, she thought. All the same, she smiled a little as she climbed the stairs. She climbed them slowly, because they were taking her away from him. She was not looking forward to a lonely night.

After nearly two hours of rest intermixed with unrest, she was startled awake by the opening of her door. Confused, she sat up, hiding her eyes from the outside light. Ross stood in the doorway, his outline dark, his robe untied and falling open to reveal his body-strength.

He came determinedly towards her, and his hands found his hips. 'I want you,' he said. 'I can't damned well sleep without you.' He bent to lift her, burying his face in her throat, inhaling the scent of her. Then he dropped her back on the bed, cast aside his robe and threw himself beside her.

Irritated by her nightgown, he eased it away from her. 'Oh, Ross, Ross,' Suzanne whispered, running her palms over his chest hair, his neck, his roughening cheeks, searching because his essential self still eluded her, 'I couldn't sleep, either.'

'Then what use is it,' he muttered, his lips roving, his hand caressing, 'sleeping apart any more?' It drifted into her mind that he might not be truly aware of what he was saying. Then, as his mouth covered hers, prising it open, the doubts crept away, to dissolve or hide, she did not know which.

Quickly, this time, as if neither could wait, they melted together. Her pulses throbbed to the beat of a timeless drum. They were lost in a love-world, climbing together to the summit and reaching it, breathless and stunned by the rapture they experienced as one, their senses reeling.

*

Suzanne awakened late, overlapping with the arrival of Mrs Hadley.

'Just leave the breakfast things, Mrs Beckett,' the housekeeper suggested. 'I'll see to everything. You'll be late for work, won't you?'

'About an hour and a half. It's a wonder Maggie hasn't phoned. If she does call when I've gone, would you mind telling her I'm on my way?'

Mrs Hadley said she would do whatever Mrs Beckett wanted.

'Where have you been?' Maggie asked, looking anxious, when Suzanne arrived at last. 'I thought you might be ill or something.'

'Sorry, Maggie.' Suzanne combed her hair. 'I over-slept.'

Maggie grinned. 'I won't ask why!'

Suzanne's smile was brilliant with happiness. Maggie laughed, but she sobered surprisingly quickly. 'Your husband called in,' she said.

Suzanne swung round, putting away her comb. A frown had taken the place of the smile. 'Why? To act the heavy boss?'

'Not really. To see how things were going, he told me. He——' she wandered towards the entrance door, 'he wasn't alone, Suzanne.'

The brilliance had gone, her eyes weren't dazzled any more. 'Who was—she, Maggie?'

Maggie turned. 'You guessed it was a "she"? His friend, he called her. Didn't tell me her name. Was she something!'

'Fair or dark?' Why did I ask? Suzanne fretted. Why should I care?

'Blonde, hair beautifully styled with a fringe, big baby-blue eyes. You know how it is with some women, the lucky so-and-so's?' She saw Suzanne glance in a mirror. 'No, not a bit like you, dear. You've got all she's got, plus something very special. I'm not very good with words. You look——' Maggie studied her face, 'kind of elusive. A man might think he's got you, but—

well, he hasn't really. You keep something to yourself.
She's all on the surface. Sorry,' with a smile, 'I've run
out of words.'

Suzanne made a face. 'Thanks, Maggie, for your
boost, but—she's got what it takes, obviously. Plus she
talks Ross's language. She's a geologist, too.'

Maggie's eyebrows shot up and down. 'Oh, forget her.
You've got him, haven't you?'

'Perhaps, but for how long? He thinks a lot of her.
They were together in Africa.'

'How much "together", Suzanne?'

Suzanne's shoulders lifted and drooped. Then the
door opened and a customer came in, and Maggie
moved forward. When the customer had gone, having
bought a waste paper basket, Maggie invited,

'Come out with Dan and me this evening. He's got a
nice brother, name of Peter. You know, blind date,
except that I know him and recommend him strongly.
Come on, it'll be fun.'

Suzanne had never felt less like 'fun' in her life.
'Thanks, but not this evening. I've got other things to
do.' Like asking Ross who the woman was, and why
was she here, in the shop? Was he thinking of putting a
woman in charge over Maggie?

During the afternoon the telephone rang, and Maggie
answered. 'For you,' she called to Suzanne. 'Frantic
mother wants daughter.'

'My mother?' Suzanne went white, picking up the
telephone. 'Mum? It's not Father?'

'He's not ill, dear, just—well, could you come round.
At once, Suzanne. It's important. Could you, dear—
please?'

# CHAPTER NINE

SUZANNE entered the living-room to find her father staring in her direction, but through her, not at her. He looked both baffled and angry, bewilderment fighting with disbelief.

Her mother looked on, hand to her mouth, seated but poised as if to move quickly. When her daughter appeared, she beckoned, as if afraid to speak.

Suzanne sat to one side of the couch. 'What's wrong, Mum?' she asked, her heart beating fast.

'What's wrong?' Her father swung round, his booming voice almost frightening her out of her wits after the deathly silence. 'He's lied to me, that's what's wrong!'

'Who has?' she queried sharply, afraid that he would say 'your husband'.

'Who? Bill Harringdon, that's who.'

'He didn't really lie, dear,' Cynthia pacified. 'He did what you were doing—or thought you were doing.'

He turned on his wife. 'Are you being disloyal to me in my hour of need? Siding with him?'

'You know I'm not, Lucas,' Cynthia answered reproachfully.

'What happened when you went to see him, Father?' Suzanne asked.

'I put my cards on the table, that's what happened. Bill, I said, I know there's a few problems to iron out before my Suzanne,' his daughter winced at the false affection, 'and your Miles are married. But we both know it's going to happen, don't we?'

Lucas was silent, rubbing a hand over his greying hair, then his face, as if to wipe away the pictures from his mind.

'And what did Bill Harringdon say?' Lucas went on. 'He said, "Of course we know, Lucas", and he slapped

me on my back. Then we'll be linked, he said, us two
family men, kith and kin and all that.'

'Then what, dear?' his wife questioned. 'You haven't
told me yet.'

Lucas walked about, round and round, as if following
the constant circle of his thoughts.

'Then he offered me a drink, told me to put my feet
on the desk, if I liked.' Lucas was sneering now. 'Well,
Bill, I said, I'll play fair with you. Soon we'll be kith
and kin, as you say. I'm being honest, Bill, I said. Since
you're going to be my daughter's father-in-law in a few
months, I'd like to ask you something. Bill sat down
then. I remember it plainly. He went a bit white. I
wondered why, but looking back, he must have guessed
what was coming.'

He was silent for some time, and Suzanne looked
anxiously at her mother. She was white, too. She wished
her father would tell them what was wrong.

'And that something is, I said,' Lucas continued at
last, 'that I badly need help financially. I've got a temporary loan, but that's short term. It's on top of my
bank loan. My company, I said, is going downhill. Only
a financial injection will stop it going bankrupt.'

'So what did Bill say?' Cynthia asked, her voice barely
audible.

'He said,' Lucas turned to her, 'he said, To tell you
the truth, Lucas, and to be perfectly honest with *you*, I
can't lend you money, none at all. You see, my business
is going down the drain, too. I need all the financial
help I can get. And do you know what he said then?'

Cynthia shook her head.

'He said, I was going to ask *you* for help with my
cash-flow problem. I was waiting until the marriage, too,
but it seems so long in happening, I'd decided to jump
the gun and ask you in advance, like you're asking me.'

Cynthia gasped, a hand spread over her mouth.
Suzanne paled, trying to work out how this turn of
events would affect her and her relationship with Ross.

'Quits—we were quits.' Lucas spoke hoarsely. All the

fight had gone, leaving him white, his legs sagging. His head turned slowly towards his daughter. 'So there'll be no marriage for you into the Harringdon family. You'll have to stay where you are.'

'You mean with Ross?'

'I mean with the man you married.' For the first time in her life, Suzanne saw her father's eyes look at her pleadingly. He looked so old, her heart lurched.

Cynthia started to go to him. Suzanne was there first, guiding him to an armchair, putting a cushion behind his head. She bent to put her hand on his as it rested, shaking, on the chair arm.

Crouching, she looked up into his face. 'I'm sorry about all this, Father. It's life, isn't it, it's the world of business.'

'Will he let you stay?'

Only this morning she would have nodded with complete certainty. Now, after all that Maggie had told her about the woman he had had with him in the shop, she could only say, 'I don't know, Father.'

Lucas's voice had wavered. His eyes were gazing at nothing. They shifted to look into the younger ones, so like his own.

There was all the child she had ever been in her now, craving to make amends, to get a good word from her father who seemed to hate her so much. 'I don't know what his plans are, Father. In fact, I still know very little about him.'

Straightening, Suzanne continued to look down at the lined face, the closed eyes. Always, all through her life—the truth hit her out of nowhere—she had tried to please not her mother, as she had thought, but her father. For as long as she could remember, she had longed to hear his approval, his acceptance of her as an intelligent, thinking creature, even though she was female, and not the son he had never had.

The only reason I've fought him over the years, she reasoned, was to hurt him as much as he was constantly hurting me. A kindly word now and then would have made the world of difference. If only her father had understood in those days, when she was so young and vulnerable. Now she was a woman. Now *she* would have to be the one to understand.

Lucas rose slowly and made for the door. Suzanne and her mother watched him go, then Suzanne sank down on to the couch.

'Be kind to him, dear,' her mother pleaded. 'He's had a terrible shock. His best friend, to let him down like that!'

'Bill Harringdon could be thinking that, too, Mother.'

Cynthia nodded but, loyal wife that she was, she could spare little sympathy for the man who had, in her view, let her husband down so badly.

'Tell Ross, won't you, Suzanne?'

'That the loan will have to continue indefinitely now? I don't know how his finances stand, Mother, but I'll do my best.'

The telephone rang, and Suzanne answered it on the extension by her father's bureau. 'Miles? Yes, I've heard—my father told me. I understand that you're sorry, Miles. Of course I forgive you. The world of business isn't always a pleasant one, is it? Yes, call me at home—my husband's home—some time.'

Suzanne turned to find her mother drying the tears from her eyes. With her arm around her mother's shoulders, she tried comforting her. For all they knew, her father might be doing the same upstairs. Men, as well as women, needed to rid their bodies of tension and disappointment somehow.

There were descending footsteps. 'He's coming,' Cynthia whispered. 'Be gentle with him, dear,' she pleaded.

'Don't worry, Mum, I'll be gentle, as you say.' Now she understood so much more about her filial relationship with her father, she could speak the words with sincerity and compassion.

*

Suzanne entered Ross's house with mixed feelings. Remembering the delight of spending the night in his arms, she felt the time could not pass quickly enough until his return. Yet knowing what she had to tell him, she was twisted into knots inside.

To ease her anxiety, she set about preparing the evening meal. Somehow, she knew he would not be late home. As a surprise, she set the table, the surface of which shone with Mrs Hadley's polishing. She used place mats and candlesticks, adding a small bowl of flowers.

Hearing the key in the door, she went into the hall, eyes shining, ready to run into Ross's arms. There was a touch about him of the old remoteness. It was chillingly familiar. He smiled with his mouth but not his eyes. She could not run into the arms of this man, whether or not they had lain entangled for most of the night's dark hours.

'Ross?' She had made his name into a question, giving away her uncertainty.

'None other. Who else had you expected?' He went straight to the living-room, making for the drinks. As he poured, he saw the dining table. 'A special guest, judging by that.'

'You're the special guest.'

His brows lifted and he raised his glass in a mocking toast. His attitude worried her. Returning to the kitchen, she tried to work out its cause. He came to stand in the doorway, shoulder against the frame, watching her over the rim of the glass. Was he waiting for her to speak? Did he somehow sense there was something troubling her—something connected with him?

When he spoke, she knew that it was connected with him, but he was on the wrong track. 'Well, aren't you going to ask me who she was?' Suzanne pretended ignorance of the subject of his question. 'No? You must be dying to know.'

'I can take a guess, Ross.' Her voice, and every feeling inside her, had gone flat. 'Your friend Tania Marlowe.

And if you expect me to play the jealous wife, you'll wait a long time. Don't tell me what she˙was doing in the town—I don't want to know.' Of course she did, desperately, but she would keep that strictly to herself.

He made a careless gesture with his empty glass that said, Okay, that's it. He put the glass down and straddled a stool at the breakfast bar, hands gripping the seat between his thighs. 'There's still something on your mind.'

'There is?' She could play cat and mouse, too. 'Did you learn mind-reading during your stay in the jungle?'

'Stop stalling and tell me!' His words were a curt order and they stung her like a whiplash. He was back to the man who had burst in on that engagement party—to stop her committing bigamy, as he'd said at the time.

His eyes were like pieces of glinting ice, and Suzanne suppressed a shiver. Putting down the serving spoon she had been holding, she obeyed his command. No point in talking round the subject to soften the impact. He would see through her tactics at once.

'All right, I'll tell you. I've just come from my parents' house, where I left my father in a state of shock.' She watched for his reaction, but there was none. 'Yesterday afternoon I called on my parents.' She slipped her hands into her apron pockets. 'I told them I——' with her tongue she moistened her lips, 'I wanted to stay married to you.'

A glance at his face told her nothing. He crossed his legs and folded his arms, seeming completely unmoved by her revelation.

'My father nearly went mad.'

Ross's smile was sardonic and faintly cruel.

'He insisted that I went on with the divorce and married Miles Harringdon. I—I refused. He tried to contact his friend Bill Harringdon, but he wasn't there. But he did see him this afternoon.'

Ross slipped from the stool, peeled off his jacket and hung it on the back of the kitchen door. He then walked about slowly, hands in pockets.

'He told Mr Harringdon everything—not about you,' she added hastily. 'About his financial difficulties and—and everything.' The faint amusement in his face worried her. 'That's when my father had a shock.'

Ross held up his hand. 'He discovered that Bill Harringdon was playing the same devious game as he was. That is, waiting until you and his precious son were married, then asking your father for the loan for which your father was asking him.' He stopped in front of her. *'Snap!'* He clicked his fingers in her face, making her jump back and her heart pound.

'How did you know?' she whispered.

'I made it my business to know. You didn't think I'd lend money blind, having no information about the man or the company to which I was lending it? Or about the man who was the father of the son to whom my wife was allowing herself to become engaged?'

'You mean you got private detectives on to them?'

'Right in one go. Are you really trying to tell me that neither you nor your father knew about Harringdon's plight? Do you really expect me to believe Harringdon's son never once mentioned his father's business was nearing bankruptcy?'

Suzanne could only shake her head. 'Miles kept talking about plans for expansion, how well they were doing, and so on.'

'So he was in on the act of fooling you, too. You'd better give him his ring back. He's probably paying for it by instalments.'

The meal would be almost ready for serving, Suzanne estimated, but she couldn't bring herself to do anything about it. From the heights they had reached this morning, they had descended to the sunless valley, and there seemed no prospect of their climbing to that incomparable summit ever again.

He stood in front of her. 'It all adds up to the fact that you've all been playing a very hazardous game. Now both companies are in danger of dissolution.'

She frowned, her mouth tightening with fear. 'Both,

Ross? You don't mean you'll call in your loan to my father?'

He saw the fear written large across her face and he smiled. It was not a pleasant smile. 'I've got you, haven't I, just where I want you.'

'Didn't those three nights we spent together mean anything, Ross?'

'Three nights together? When you told me ad nauseam that you loved me? I've spent thirty nights with some women, and they've meant nothing. Why should three with you matter to me?'

He might as well have got hold of her body and wrung it like a wet rag. To him, she had been just another woman!

'I'm your wife, Ross,' she whispered, her face white.

'Are you? For how long? While the loan lasts? You only came back to me under the condition I imposed.'

'When I said I loved you, Ross, I meant it.'

'Did you?' His mouth twisted. 'Did you tell Harringdon you loved him when you went to bed with him?'

She shook her head helplessly under the string of accusations, but he went on relentlessly.

'It was for money all the time, wasn't it?' he attacked. 'You agreed to marry him—while still married to me, be it noted—for the loan your father wanted from his father. When I demanded you back as a surety for my loan to your father, you came to me.'

'Because I'd discovered I still loved you, had never stopped, in fact.'

'An opportune discovery, if I may say so,' he grated. 'All the same, you continued to tell me you intended starting divorce proceedings—only to change your mind, probably on the orders of your father, who by then had begun to have doubts about his old friend Bill Harringdon's true financial status.'

'You're wrong, Ross. My father had no doubts at all, until Bill told him this afternoon.'

'Do you really expect me to believe that piece of fiction? If I took the trouble to look into both companies' affairs, your father—who's no fool, despite his blustering—would also have taken that precaution.'

'So you're accusing me of complicity?' Suzanne queried, her voice hoarse.

'I'm saying you've been in league with your father from start to finish.'

That, she thought, putting a shaking hand to her head, was the bitterest irony of all. Hadn't the reason come to her only today why she had always done her utmost to please her father, that reason being to gain his affection and praise?

'Carrying out his wishes.' She had spoken to herself, but Ross took her up.

'It's the same thing. Don't split hairs.'

She went to the sink and took a drink of water, rinsing the glass. 'If you must know, I was thinking thoughts——' she faced him, 'thoughts which you, with your insensitivity, wouldn't understand in a million years.'

'You're saying I'm insensitive?'

'To your very depths. I don't know what happened to your character when you were in the heart of the African jungle, but take it from me, Ross, it's changed almost beyond recognition.'

'I'll tell you what happened. Bitterness happened.'

'You can't forget and forgive?'

'I can't forget, nor——' with a flash of his eyes, 'can I forgive.'

Suzanne lifted her shoulders hopelessly. 'There's nothing more to be said, is there?'

He went to the entrance door from the garden and stared out. She turned off the heat on the cooker, hoping the food would not be entirely ruined. Staring unseeingly at the pots and pans, she felt a leaden weight somewhere in the region of her heart.

'When—when I came home, I thought I'd cook us a really nice meal.' Her voice was thickening. She had to clear it. 'Just for us two. This morning, I'd felt so happy, I . . .' She could not go on.

Ross did not turn or speak.

Controlling her emotions, she went on, 'Coming home in the mood you did, I wonder why you bothered. In fact,' she continued after a while, 'I wonder what draws you back each day. After all, it takes more than bricks and mortar and wood and work to make a home.'

He turned from the window to lean back against it. 'And what else does it take?'

She looped her long hair behind her ears and kept her eyes averted from him. 'It takes love, and by your reckoning, there's no love here.' Ross still did not respond. She picked up a serving spoon, put it down. 'Have you ever thought what a powerful force "home" is? The thought of it draws people from whatever part of the world they might be. Have you ever thought why?'

Ross folded his arms. 'The idea of treading on their own patch of ground, maybe? Their house and their own roof over their head?'

'Or a person?' Her voice had gone small. She had not bargained for the explosive effect it might have on him.

Three strides brought him to her. He gripped a handful of her hair, pulled her head back with it. She saw his teeth clenched, the anger in his eyes. His face was frighteningly near. 'Do you think I don't know? Six years away from my home country. Thousands of miles from the girl I married!'

He was hurting her, but she would not plead mercy. His inability to forgive was terrifying her. Her only weapons were hard-hitting words. 'You told me yourself you didn't go short on women, so why did it bother you that I was so far away?'

His hands moved to clasp her head, forcing it back. 'I must have been mad,' he ground out, 'I must have been crazy!' His hands pressed so hard, they were distorting her features. Her mouth was open on a gasp of pain. 'Please,' she begged, 'please . . .'

The light of revenge was in his eyes as his mouth descended, his lips cruelly hard on hers, their teeth grinding together. His arm felt like steel around her waist as, in his fury, he drew blood from her lip.

She heard a sob and knew it came from her throat. The sound must have touched a chord, since he let her go and she slumped on to a stool, covering her face. There was a sound and she looked up.

He was finishing his drink, looking down at her, his face a mask. He half-threw the glass on a table and made for the stairs, climbing them fast. Suzanne's legs felt weak but she made the living-room, sinking to the couch and lying back on it.

It was some time later that he entered the room. She did not open her eyes, although she felt that he was looking at her. At last he asked, 'Shall I serve the meal?'

'I'm not hungry any more, thank you,' she answered tiredly. 'But help yourself to anything you want.'

There were footsteps and she felt him standing beside the couch. Her eyes opened and her cheeks warmed at the expression on his face. 'I could, couldn't I?' His eyes skimmed the length of her. 'Right here.'

Her legs swung to the floor and she pushed at her hair, trying to smooth it. 'I must look a mess!'

Ross sat beside her. 'Are you fishing for compliments?'

'Not from you, thanks. Not after all you've said, doubting my integrity, lowering me to the status of one of your women.'

He did not react and she looked at him. His smile was faint and maddeningly enigmatic. It went with the rest of him. His jacket was on again. He hadn't shed his business executive skin.

He put his hand palm upward in the space between them. His smile was an invitation now. Suzanne looked at his hand, then at him, then with deliberation, she got to her feet and made for the door.

He was up and after her, spinning her round and pulling her into his arms. He placed small, exciting kisses all over her face, even her eyes, then touching down on her parted, half-smiling lips. He was healing the wounds he had inflicted and coaxing her to yield all at the same time.

When she was pliant in his arms, he lifted his head but kept his body pressed against her. They were smiling at each other when the door bell rang, and with a curse, he let her go.

'For you or me?' Her hands gestured, telling him, I don't know.

Running to the window which overlooked the drive, she stared out. Oh no, she thought, not Miles!

Hurrying to open the door, she found that Ross was there first. He was back at the top of his mountain, remote, unreachable. 'Your visitor, not mine.'

Miles hesitated, looking at them, plainly feeling the hostility in the air. 'Is it inconvenient?' he asked uncertainly.

'Of course not, Miles. I——' Suzanne cursed the compulsion which made her glance at Ross as if for permission. 'I wanted to see you. I forgot to tell you on the phone this afternoon.'

'Excuse me, please,' Ross said frigidly to Miles, who blocked the exit.

'Where are you going?' Suzanne asked. There was the note of anxiety now, letting her down.

'Out. What does it look like?'

'But the meal, Ross—I've cooked for two!'

'I'm dining with a friend. Did I forget to tell you?' The curl of his lips told her that he knew he was hurting her. 'Give my portion to your *friend*.' Then he was gone.

In the living-room, Miles stood looking about him, his darting eyes taking in superficialities, revealing his discomfiture. 'Nice place. Were you two quarrelling?'

'Yes and no. On and off.' She managed a laugh, but quickly sobered, being torn by an undercurrent of doubt. Where was Ross going? Who was the 'friend' with whom he was dining? Who else, she answered herself, but the fair-haired woman he had shown round the shop?

'You said you wanted to see me. What about?'

It would have been tactless to have said bluntly, Your ring, to give it back. So she compromised with, 'Oh, lots of things. Please sit down.'

He did so, not yet at ease.

'It was true about the food, Miles. Could you help me out and eat some of it?'

'Well, I was going to invite you out to a meal, but yes, thank you very much. It's kind of you.'

Why was Miles so stiff and strained? 'If you're worried about what's been going on between our two fathers, Miles, then please stop. I expect your father's explained everything to you like my father did to me?' Miles nodded. 'Shall we leave it at that, then?'

'It was an awful thing to do to you, Suzanne,' Miles burst out. 'I really did—do—like you, you know, but——'

'Let's stay friends, then, shall we?'

Miles nodded without smiling. It seemed that nothing she could do was able to make him relax.

'The ring you gave me—I'll get it.' She went to the door, saying, 'Help yourself to a drink. They're over there.'

'No, thanks,' he called after her.

Suzanne was down in a few moments, holding out the ring box. Miles thanked her, flicking open the lid and staring a little sadly at the gemstones. His thoughts did not seem to be on the ring, but he slipped the box into his pocket.

'Come on,' Suzanne caught his hand, 'let's eat. Help me carry in the dishes. We're doing it in style this evening.'

He passed the dining alcove, staring. 'Candles? Were you expecting a visitor?'

You're the special guest, she'd told Ross, never dreaming he already had a dinner date.

'Only my—Ross.' Had she sounded casual enough?

'Were you celebrating something?'

If only they had been! 'Maybe, maybe not. I thought we were, but——' she sighed.

'I should have known I couldn't win against him.' He sounded so sad Suzanne laughed and kissed his cheek. To her amazement, Miles drew away.

'Don't do that, Suzanne.'

'Why not, Miles? Is there a law against it, now I've returned your ring?'

'I like it too much, that's why,' he answered fiercely.

Suzanne stared in astonishment. It was the greatest amount of emotion he had ever exhibited in front of her. She moved her left hand to pick up the oven gloves. Miles must have seen the flash of the diamonds.

'He's given you an engagement ring, now, has he?'

'You mustn't sound so bitter, Miles. When we were married, we were too poor for Ross to give me one.'

Miles followed Suzanne as she carried a steaming dish into the dining-room. As they ate the meal in the light of the candles, he told her about his father's secretary. 'Her parents have plenty of money. My father told me I must ask her out. You know the rest.'

'So it's starting all over again? First you with me, now you with——' She pushed at her empty plate. 'Are you going to allow your father to use you again, Miles?'

'It wasn't really a case of using me with you, Suzanne. I really wanted to marry you.' He moved his knife and fork to a different angle. 'I wasn't pretending when I kissed you.'

Her hand reached out for his. 'I'm sorry, really sorry, Miles. I had no idea. You never told me.'

'I planned to, once you'd got that divorce.'

He did not stay long after dinner. They drank their coffee, talking impersonally, keeping away from family matters. When he got up to go, he said,

'How do you feel about being tied to your husband for an indefinite length of time?'

Suzanne frowned, twisting her new ring. 'I don't know. Sometimes I'm happy, sometimes I'm so miserable I want to cry. Living abroad has done something to him—hardened him. Yet, at other times,' she avoided Miles' eyes since she could not bear to see the hurt, 'he's so—well, like he used to be.'

Miles nodded, held out his hand and pulled her towards him. His kiss was harder and more determined than any he had given her before. After that, it seemed he could not speak. He lifted his hand, let himself out and drove away.

Later, Suzanne went to bed. For a while she sat up reading, telling herself that she wasn't listening for Ross's return, only that she didn't feel tired enough to settle down.

When she did turn out the light and try to sleep, it would not come. It wouldn't come because Ross didn't come: it was that simple. In the end, her body's need for sleep overcame her mind's resistance, but it was about two hours later that she stirred.

Anxiety as to whether he was home yet made her fully alert. Before she could sleep again, she had to know. Scrambling out of bed, she ran across the room and on to the landing. Ross's door was open and the bedroom was in darkness.

Tiptoeing in, she saw the bed had not been touched. Nor was there a light from his bathroom, or the main bathroom. There was no sound from downstairs. Returning slowly to her own room, Suzanne sank on to the bed. How could there be any doubt about it? Ross was staying the night with his girl-friend.

The house had never felt so empty as she ate her toast and drank her coffee next morning. Her limbs felt heavy, too, and her brain clouded.

Maggie did not miss her friend's lacklustre appearance. 'Had a night on the tiles?' she asked jauntily as Suzanne combed her hair behind the screen. When she saw Suzanne's lip tremble, Maggie apologised. 'Forget I mentioned it. I enjoyed myself last night with Dan. We went out for a meal, then went dancing. Dan's brother, Peter, said he'd like to meet you.'

'That was nice of him, but——' Suzanne held out her wedding finger, saying without words, I'm married.

'Hey, you're wearing a new ring. I didn't notice.' Maggie studied it. 'Is that something! Ross? But why?'

'He couldn't afford to buy me one in the early days.'

'So he's bought you one now, in spite of the odd sort of arrangement you two have got? I mean, Ross with his blonde, you with Miles.'

'Not any more. Miles accepted his ring back last night, reluctantly. His father's told him he must chase another girl, one whose parents have plenty of money. She's his father's secretary.'

Maggie laughed. 'Poor Miles! Surely he refused?'

'At the moment, he doesn't know whether he's coming or going.' Suzanne frowned. 'Nor do I. Maggie, Ross stayed out last night. He just didn't come home.'

'So that's the reason for your out-on-the-tiles look— lack of sleep through worrying. Who was he with, Suzanne?'

Suzanne shrugged listlessly. 'He said he was dining out with a "friend".'

'Sex of friend not mentioned? Well, there's hope, isn't there? Could have been a business colleague from abroad, maybe.'

Suzanne took a duster into the shop and started work.

As she drew up in the drive that evening, she sat for a few moments trying to collect her thoughts. Fatigue lay heavily across her shoulders. The empty night of waiting had caught up with her at last. For a few moments she let it wash over her, resting her head on her bare arm which lay across the steering wheel.

Even so, she could not relax. Doubts were plaguing her. What should she say to Ross when he got home? Something like, 'Did you enjoy your night with your girl-friend? Was the hotel bed comfortable?' Or should she behave as though nothing out of the ordinary had happened?

The noise of a car braking beside hers had her head shooting up. Ross was home, and her heart was tattooing out a welcome—until she saw his passenger; and the light in her eyes died right away. This must be the woman he had taken into the shop yesterday. There was

no doubting that her appearance deserved all the praise
Maggie had given it. One thing she doubted, however.
Maggie had remarked that 'she was all on the surface'.
A single glance at the woman's face told her she had
depths which would defy the most probing of minds.

Ross was out of the car and coming round to his
passenger's side. But it was Suzanne he turned to first.
'Something wrong?' he asked. 'Aren't you feeling well?'

'I'm all right, thank you,' she replied, her mouth taut.
You, she thought, don't look as if you'd spent most of
last night nagged by worries about me as I was about you.

The woman passenger was getting out of the car.
'Ross?' She looked up at him, smiling. Who is this
woman? she was asking. Suzanne joined them between
the cars.

'Suzanne, this is Tania Marlowe, the friend I told you
about. Tania, my wife, Suzanne.' He had spoken
abruptly, but Tania Marlowe was still smiling and holding out her hand.

'Mrs Beckett, I've heard so much about you.'

The standard introductory cliché, Suzanne thought
acidly. She managed a smile and answered, 'Ross has
talked about you, too. And please call me Suzanne.'

The delicately pencilled brows rose, the grey eyes
sought his. 'Not too much, I hope.'

Suzanne answered for him. 'Not too much, Miss
Marlowe. Discretion is his second name.'

Tania laughed, seeming unflurried. 'Make it Tania,
Suzanne.' She looked towards the house. 'What an attractive residence, Ross. I hope there's something good
sizzling in the oven—I'm starving!'

If Ross's girl-friend possessed a large appetite,
Suzanne reflected, it certainly did not show in her shape.
The woman was surely so slim her figure would hardly
catch a man's eye, let alone his interest.

'Suzanne?' Ross was speaking. 'Did you prepare anything before you left home this morning?'

If they'd been alone, she thought, I would have told
him just what I thought of him for putting me in the wrong

so cleverly. He must know that's something I never do.

Sweetly, she answered, head on one side, 'I thought you might be home before me, darling, and start the meal as you usually do. Anyway,' she looked at his guest, who seemed just a little anxious, 'I wasn't aware, was I, that you would be bringing a visitor.'

They started walking towards the house. 'Ross, you surely didn't forget to tell your wife I would be coming?' Tania asked huskily.

'I didn't tell her.' He had the key in the lock and was showing them in.

'Sorry, Tania,' Suzanne said, 'there's no meal waiting for us. Please make yourself comfortable while I wash my hands and get down to the food.'

'I'll show Tania to her room.' Ross gestured her to the door.

Suzanne jerked round to gaze at Ross unbelievingly. At that moment Tania was on her way and did not see her hostess's parted lips and staring eyes. Ross gazed back, his face telling her nothing.

As they reached the stairs, Suzanne heard Tania say, 'You'll bring my case in later, will you, darling?'

Suzanne sank on to a chair. Ross had brought his girl-friend to stay the night? And without consulting her?

Forcing herself into the kitchen, she prepared food like a robot, as if programmed to do so. 'I'll help.' Ross was entering the kitchen, having removed his jacket. If I were really his wife, she thought, instead of a temporary one, I'd run up to him, put my arms round his neck and ask for his reassuring kiss.

Which of your women, she would joke, were you with last night? She would have known, since he would have told her, that he'd be away from home entertaining an overseas guest somewhere, too far away, in fact, to get back for the night.

Instead, she threw his politeness back at him. 'Thank you. I could do with some.'

'Tania's in the apartment, through the door to the modern wing.'

'One night or two?' she asked.

'Three, maybe four.'

Suzanne almost choked. 'You mean you've brought her here as a guest without telling me?'

'Is there any reason why I should have told you? Did you tell me that Harringdon was coming to spend the evening with you?'

'I would have told you—if I'd known he was coming.' There was a brittle silence as they worked side by side. 'I gave him back his ring.'

'Did his clawing hand reach out and grab it?'

'He was very upset,' she chided, reproaching him for his nastiness.

The knife he was using clattered down. 'Poor bloody swine!' he snarled. 'Do you want me to weep for him? You don't think it was losing you that upset him, do you? It was the thought of all that money he was convinced you represented walking out of his arms.'

'Do you need to be so unpleasant about him? He told me last night he really wanted to marry me. He hadn't told me before how he felt, because he was waiting for the divorce.'

Ross's hands were clenched on his hips. 'Last night he told you, did he? So he stayed on. I thought he might. It was one of the reasons I absented myself from the house—or didn't you notice?'

Suzanne carried on with her work. She hoped he wouldn't see that her hands were shaking.

'I trust you slept well,' he went on implacably, 'afterwards.' He gripped her shoulders and pulled her round. 'But you look as though you overdid it. You should have told him you were a working girl. You should have set the alarm for him to stop his activities.' His grip tightened, his teeth snapped. 'You should also have reminded him you were a married woman.'

He threw her from him and rubbed his hands on his clothes as if to cleanse them. Tearing off her apron, Suzanne bundled it and threw it at him, and it dropped to the ground. Her voice was thick, her eyes brimming as she hit back.

'I'm not staying here listening to your insults. You make me sick, Ross. I just don't like you any more. I wish you'd never come back into my life. As far as I'm concerned, you can go right out of it again—and take your woman with you!'

His hand lifted as if aiming for her cheek, but she jerked her head out of his reach, sobbing. 'Be your own chef and servant to your guest, because I won't, not after all those terrible things you've said to me!'

She ran out of the room, making for the stairs. Pausing for breath halfway up, she looked down and saw that he was watching her. His eyes were blazing with a consuming fire. If they had been alone, she knew he would have unleashed that fire on her and it would have seared her to her innermost being.

Some time later, there was a tap on her door. Something prevented her from shouting. Go away. If it had been Ross, he would have walked in. 'Yes?' she asked.

The door opened and Tania stood there, her face freshly made-up, her dress rose-pink and slim-fitting. 'May I come in?' Suzanne nodded, dabbing at her eyes. Tania said, 'I'm so sorry for what's happened. If I'd known Ross hadn't told you, I'd have phoned you myself. I certainly didn't mean to cause you two to quarrel over me.'

'That's all right.' What else could she say? The woman seemed sincere in her apologies. She couldn't have told her, Ross and I are in a constant state of quarrelling.

'The meal is ready. He sent me to tell you.'

Suzanne nodded and murmured her thanks. She managed a smile. 'I'll wring myself dry and make an appearance.'

Tania nodded, returning her smile. Alone again, Suzanne washed and dried her face, frowning. She wanted to hate the woman, but how could she dislike such a pleasant person?

As the meal progressed, Suzanne realised that the hate she could not feel for Tania had manifested itself in another way—a form of resentment. Listening to Ross and his guest discussing their experiences while abroad, talking about their shared subject so technically, forced her to realise how wide the gulf really was between herself and her husband.

If she had been allowed to go back to him through love and not compulsion, she could have tried, couldn't she? Surely there were books around which a layman could read and understand, books for children on the subject, or the amateur geologist?

'Suzanne?' Ross was recalling her from the maelstrom of her thoughts, and she looked up, taken unawares. 'Tania was talking about the shop.'

Tania smiled. 'You were miles away.'

No, right here, Suzanne almost corrected her. 'Oh, yes—Maggie's shop: I mean,' with a glance at Ross, 'your shop.'

'Ours,' he stated, his underbrowed stare daring her to disagree.

'You make things for it, Ross said.'

'Now and then,' Suzanne answered Tania carelessly. 'It gives me something to do.' Her glance this time at Ross was spiced with mischief. 'A kind of therapy.'

'Therapy?' Tania's grey eyes widened. Suzanne could see the attraction she held for Ross. 'Little-girl look,' Maggie had said—and there it was. 'Why, are you recovering from something?'

Suzanne laughed, looking down at her empty dish and resting her elbows on the table, supporting her chin with her linked hands. Yes, she thought in answer, from the effects of this sham of a marriage Ross and I have. He thinks I love Miles, whereas I really love him. He doesn't love me, but I do know he loves you. He must do, otherwise you wouldn't be here.

To Tania, she said, 'I didn't mean it. I enjoy working with my hands. I make small things that children buy for their mothers or aunties.'

'Oh, I see. Children.' Tania looked thoughtfully at her own ringless hands. 'They're something I suppose

you two will be thinking about some time?' Her comment elicited no answer. 'Ross?'

Why is she probing? Suzanne thought, distressed.
Doesn't she know the true position between us?

'Certainly, one day,' Ross was saying. 'There's a room
not so far from your apartment that's been put aside
for use as a nursery.' His eyes shifted to Suzanne.
'Hasn't there, darling?'

'Has there?' Tania was looking so surprised, Suzanne
was forced to add, 'Of course there has. One day, in the
distant future, I suppose it will be occupied.'

'Oh, I get it,' Tania exclaimed. 'You're not too keen
to start a family yet. You want to make up for the lost
years.'

'Yes, yes,' Suzanne answered with some impatience,
then softened the impact of her tone with a smile, which
she transferred from Tania to Ross.

It was he who then became the impatient one and
pushed back his chair.

'You two run away,' Suzanne advised them jokingly.
'I'll play mother and clear the dishes. After all, you two
cooked the meal.'

Tania wandered into the living area. Ross caught
Suzanne's chin and pushed her face upwards. 'What the
hell do you think you're playing at?'

Suzanne opened her eyes over-wide and threw back
with mock-innocence, 'I don't know what you're talking
about.' Her chin was discarded and Ross went after
Tania.

'I'll get your case and bag from the car,' he called, at
which Tania declared that she would help him.

When they had gone, Suzanne drooped. The thrust
and play of the conversation had brought into being
tensions which had been so deep-seated she had not been
aware of them until now.

Children, they'd said, the nursery, the future ...
Didn't Tania really know that the children for whom
that nursery was intended were not Ross's wife's, but
hers, *hers*?

# CHAPTER TEN

SUZANNE had washed the dishes and tidied everything away, yet Ross had not reappeared to offer his help. She sat in an armchair, looking through a magazine, waiting for him and his guest to join her. They were so long in making their appearance, she realised that they were not coming.

A restlessness descended and she put aside the magazine. She would go to her bedroom and look out her workbox; that at least would give her something to do, she decided. As she pulled the box from the cupboard, she remembered the room which Ross had told her was hers to use as she liked.

The fact that the apartment which Tania was going to occupy was also in the modern section had nothing at all to do, Suzanne told herself, with her sudden decision to start using the room.

Gathering her workbox and basket-weaving materials on to a tray, she pushed with her shoulder at the dividing door. The door to Tania's apartment stood wide open and Suzanne could hear the talking and laughter.

Curiosity overrode her determination not to glance in. Ross was seated in a deep armchair opposite the door, glass in his hand, his legs outstretched and crossed casually. To Suzanne's annoyance, she found her feet slowing down. Ross turned to look at her, his eyes lazy, and made a 'come on in' movement with his head.

Suzanne ignored it, continuing on her way. 'Suzanne!' he called sharply.

'Yes?' She had paused without retracing her steps.

'Come and join us. Tania's brought a bottle of champagne.'

I hope it chokes her, was Suzanne's first thought. Uncharitable it may have been, she accepted, but it gave

157

her some satisfaction. Slowly, she returned to stand in the doorway. 'It's kind of you, but no, thanks.'

Tania appeared. 'Yes, please come in,' she invited, 'and make yourself comfortable.'

Shock was followed by a twisting ache in her stomach as she saw that her husband's guest had changed. There was no doubting that Tania had made herself 'comfortable'. Her fair hair had been brushed until it shone and her bare feet peeped from the hem of the turquoise-coloured, ankle-length housegown.

Who was Tania's quarry? Suzanne wondered. Then she told herself to stop being so naïve. He was sitting right there, as comfortable and at home as if he belonged there—and to the woman who, it seemed, was entertaining him.

Suzanne indicated the overflowing tray she held. 'I'm going along to my work-room.'

'Really?' Tania seemed genuinely interested. 'What will all that become when it's finished?'

'A pot plant holder.' With a smiling nod at Tania and a nod without the smile at her husband, Suzanne went on her way. Her thoughts were dark. The woman, she told herself, should be an actress, not a geologist. Her only true interest was in my departure, not my hobby.

Ross had added other furniture without telling her. There were upright chairs and a couple of armchairs, a fitted carpet had been laid in a dusky pink. Curtains had been hung to match. Flowers stood in a vase, probably put there by Mrs Hadley.

The overall effect was so pleasing, Suzanne found herself wishing she had made use of the room before. It was not only a work-place now, as Ross had suggested, but a kind of hideaway. Recalling the almost domestic scene she had just left, she knew that she had never needed a hideaway so much as now.

Putting down the tray, she sorted through the contents. To her dismay, she became aware that the restlessness which she had felt downstairs had not left her. It had even reached her fingers, making their movements jerky.

Maybe it was resentment, she reasoned. Maybe her hands wanted to claw something—preferably, she thought with a gleam, her husband's face—rather than be made to work to the instructions of her irritable brain.

Impatiently, she left the table and went to the window. It was dark now, but the moon had risen, painting the greenery with a light, white hand. Even the blue-tinted pool had been bleached by it, but it beckoned irresistibly.

That's what I'll do, she thought, work away my restlessness or whatever it is that's prickling my nervous system, by swimming and exercising it out of me. Walking carefully back along the corridor, she found that the apartment's entrance door had been closed.

With hands that had been made extra-powerful with a terrible, crying jealousy, she pushed at the swing door and ran to her room. Stripping fast, she took her white swimsuit from a drawer and put it on, covering it with a robe.

Slipping on sandals and taking a large towel from the bathroom, she sped down the stairs. Stepping lightly through the living-room, she unbolted the patio doors. Moving round the two basket chairs and running down the garden to the pool's deepest part, she dropped the towel and stepped out of her sandals.

Contemplating the ruffled surface, she paused for only seconds before shedding the robe and shallow-diving straight into the water, making a moon-splash which she was sure they could hear in the house. Floating for a moment, she listened, hearing only the ruffling leaves in the breeze.

Then she turned over and swam. All the suppressed energy inside her spilled over to mingle with the cool, silvered waters. Again and again she swam from one end to the other, until all the restlessness had left her and she was left enervated but content, floating wherever the water took her.

There was a movement from the house which alerted

her senses. In the semi-darkness, she lifted her head and stared. There was the outline of a man seated in one of the chairs. His legs were crossed and his head fixed as he stared unmoving in her direction.

Gritting her teeth, Suzanne thought, I'll show him! She did not stop to ask the question, Show him what? Again she swam, but this time she had to force her limbs to move. On and on she went until she realised how cold the water was, how fatigued she had become and how much she wanted to drag herself from the water and lie down to rest.

In the end, her body forced her to give in. She clambered out, ignored the watching man and wrapped the towel around her, dropping to the damp grass and lying there, gasping for breath. It was a little while before she realised that he had come down the garden to stand beside her.

'Why are you lying down there?' His voice was deep and controlled. 'Enticing me to join you,' he crouched down, 'unwrap you,' he started to peel the towel away, 'and make love to you?'

Suzanne did not answer. Instead she lay there, letting him talk. He lifted her arm, only to find it hanging limply. He lifted her head, only to discover that it hung back. He spoke to her sharply, and her eyelids flickered open. His face is so near, she thought, yet he's so far, so very far away.

He took her hands and pulled her to a sitting position, then all the way to her feet. He pulled her against him and enclosed her in his arms, demanding, 'For God's sake, what's wrong? Are you ill?'

'No,' she whispered, her arms round his waist, her head against his shoulder, 'just tired, very tired.' His shirt was partly open, the sleeves rolled.

'You idiot girl, coming out here, in this temperature, and swimming as if you were training for the Olympics!'

His hand stroked her soaking hair, running over her shoulders, down her back, finding her hips inside the briefs and seeking the softness of her stomach. When his mouth sought hers, she gave it to him, unable to help herself.

Her flesh began to burn under his touch, only to turn, in a second, to shaking. Ross picked up the towel and wrapped it round her, flinging her robe over his shoulder. She was swung into his arms and carried into the house. He paused to secure the patio door, then continued on his way to her bedroom.

Setting her on her feet, he unwrapped her again and started to dry her. He felt behind her back for the bra-top fastening, but she grasped his arms, protesting. Easily he freed himself, then let the swimming top fall to the carpet. When he bent to ease the briefs away, Suzanne made no effort to protest.

All she had wanted, since the last time he had loved her, was to feel his touch on her cool skin again. Now he rubbed her briskly, bringing a glowing warmth to her mind as well as her body. He lifted the towel to rub at her hair, and her head was pushed back under the pressure.

His eyes slipped down to hers, and brown and blue were locked in love-play. The towel dropped away and she stood naked in the circle of his arms. Her hands reached blindly for his shirt buttons, unfastening the rest. Then he caught her to him, pressing her head against his chest while his hands cupped and caressed her breasts.

She found herself kissing his skin, her hands gripping the sides of his neck, then pushing upward to his hair. Ross scooped her into his arms, raising her so that his lips could tease the enticing points peaking the yielding fullness.

He lowered her to the bed, pulling off his shirt and unfastening his waistband. As he stretched beside her, he reached out, pulling her on to her side. His piercing eyes burned like the sweltering sun in a blue sky and there was an essentially male look about him which told of a masculine world which he inhabited and into which he had taken her to join him.

He rolled on to her, his leg over hers, while his hands found intimate places, bringing her body arching to him in ecstatic surrender. His mouth had long taken control of hers, exploring its sweetness and making it entirely his.

When his need of her could be denied no longer, he moulded her to him and they reached the cloud again, treading its golden aura as if they were one.

It was when it was over and they lay separated, but just as closely entwined, that Suzanne's mind began to function. Ross had made love to her despite their earlier quarrel, despite the insults they had hurled at each other.

I just don't like you any more, she'd cried out at him. Which was as bad an untruth as she had ever told. She not only liked but loved him, more and more each day, except that that was simply impossible. Yet he had not once uttered the words, I love you, not since that wonderful first year of their marriage.

Now he had brought his woman, or woman friend, as he preferred to call her, into the house to stay who knew how long? The little scene she had witnessed that evening had been so intimate, as if Ross and she had known each other in every sense of the word.

'Ross?' It was something she had to know. He stirred, but not from sleeping, more from satiation, really. He drew her even closer, nuzzling her neck. She shivered at the feelings his lips were provoking, but she could not rest until she knew.

'Yes, Suzanne?' his muffled voice mocked.

'Will you tell me something?'

He was still, then lifted his head. 'Tell you what?'

'When you were abroad and worked with Tania, did you ever——' How could she ask such a question?

'Make love to her? Is that what you want to know?' He had moved away now. No part of them made contact. His hands were lifted to cushion his head.

'That was the question I was going to ask,' she told him, holding on to her breath.

His arm descended to rest carelessly across her breasts. 'You shouldn't have asked, my own.' His voice had grown hard. 'The answer is yes. Now what will you do? Divorce me? Or,' he raised himself on to his elbow and flicked her flushed and shapely flesh with a touch of insolence, 'shall I divorce you?'

## CHAPTER ELEVEN

FOR the next few days, the question Ross had flung at her haunted Suzanne unceasingly. Was that his real intention, she was perpetually wondering, thus freeing himself to marry Tania?

He had left her bedroom almost at once, pulling on his clothes and leaving her wakeful and wondering—and desolate. Why had she ever asked that question about his relationship with his girl-friend? Shouldn't she have reasoned with herself that the past was history, gone for ever? But had it gone? What if his affair with Tania had never ended?

Suzanne hardly saw Ross. In the mornings, he and Tania had breakfasted and gone by the time she herself went downstairs. In the evenings, it seemed that they dined out, since she had her evening meals alone.

Did it mean, she wondered unhappily, that since he had told her about his past relationship with Tania, their love affair had ceased to be a secret shared and they were being more open about it? It must be so, she thought, because at night he never came to her now. It could surely mean only one thing—that he went to Tania instead.

At the shop, Maggie accepted with resignation her friend's frequent silences. 'I wish I could help you,' she had said when Suzanne had first explained the situation. 'All I know is that I'll be eternally grateful to him for taking all the business worries off my shoulders.'

It was almost the end of a seemingly unending week and Maggie was serving a customer. A feeling of weakness made Suzanne drop into a chair at the table behind the screen and put her head down on her arms. The build-up of tension was threatening to burst through the dam she had put against the force of her emotions.

164

Tania's stay seemed to be continuing indefinitely. The strain of being polite to her was becoming an impossible charade. The resentment she felt at the woman's presence was building up to such an extent that at times, in her own room, she would find her hands shaking.

If she did not give rein to her fury soon, she knew that the eventual explosion would cause a permanent split in her marriage to Ross, loan or no loan to her father. Her love for Ross could stand the strain—nothing would destroy that—but her emotions and her body could not.

The customer left and Maggie appeared. 'Oh, dear,' she said, 'we're as near breaking point as that, are we?' Suzanne lifted her head and stared dry-eyed but drained of colour at her friend. 'Let it go, dear. Keeping it all inside can only harm you. Go on, weep. I'll take over for the rest of the day.'

Suzanne shook her head slowly. 'If he divorces me, Maggie, I don't know what I'll do.'

'He didn't mean it, you know. It was a form of male self-defence coming into operation. And pride, probably. I mean, instead of you being able to hold the threat of divorcing him over his head, he decided to turn the tables and hang *his* threat over your head. Just to let you know how it felt.'

'I'd like to believe that, but I can't. It's because he wants to marry Tania, I know it! Maggie,' she turned in the chair, 'I can't face going home this evening. It's over a week now since she came, yet Ross told me she'd only be here a couple of days.'

'Tell her to go?' Maggie suggested, trying to be helpful. 'No? Tell him to choose—say it's either her or you?'

Suzanne's eyes widened. 'I dare not. What if he chooses her? Then I'd be the one who'd have to get out and the consequences of that—I haven't told you the full story—would be devastating.' She sighed. 'I think I'll have a meal out, go to see a film, maybe, then creep in late. They'll be so engrossed in each other, they won't even hear me.'

'If you think that of your husband, then you're mis-judging him badly, aren't you? The little I know about his character tells me a different story, and you'd be the one to get hurt, and I do mean hurt.'

Suzanne's head, aching now, found her arms again.

'I know,' Maggie exclaimed, 'come home with me. Dan's coming to a meal, but he won't mind. We've not planned to go anywhere special.'

Suzanne looked at her with grateful eyes. 'Are you sure?'

'Quite sure.' She looked at the wall clock. 'It's almost time to shut up shop. You put on a bit of colour and comb your hair, and——' The door opened. 'I'll serve this customer, then that's it for the day.'

Maggie invited Suzanne to follow her into her little house. It wasn't old, she often claimed, but it wasn't new. 'It's just right for me, plus Dan when we're married.' She breathed in. 'Take a sniff of that. Can my Dan cook!'

'You've got him well trained.' Maggie laughed, re-moving her jacket and fluffing her hair. Suzanne finished, almost to herself, 'Ross cooks well, too.'

Maggie glanced at her with a touch of sadness, then opened her arms to the smiling man who appeared at the kitchen door. After a greeting which, Suzanne was certain, had been shortened considerably through her own presence there, Maggie made the introductions.

After the smiling welcome, Dan, who was of medium height and had a few touches of grey in his short-cut hair, looked worried. 'I cooked for three,' he told Maggie, 'because Peter said he might drop in.'

'That's okay,' Maggie declared comfortably, 'Suzanne can share my portion. We're not big eaters, are we?' she said to her friend.

Suzanne agreed, thankful for Maggie's tact. Lately, her appetite had been smaller than usual, a fact Maggie had noticed.

'Peter's my brother,' Dan told Suzanne. 'He's a junior officer in the Merchant Navy. Got the sailor's usual roving eye.' He glanced at her wedding ring. 'I'll have to warn him off you!'

'He won't get anywhere with my friend here,' Maggie told Dan. 'Now, if you want to wash, Suzanne, the bathroom's upstairs and turn right.'

Suzanne was combing her hair when Dan's brother arrived. She heard the sound of laughter without a stir of emotion. Her thoughts were at home, wondering whether Ross and his girl-friend were there and if he had even noticed his wife's absence.

The dress she wore was short-sleeved, pale blue and zipped from a close-fitting waist to the deep collar at the neckline. It was simply-styled but attractive and one she wore often for work.

Maggie's voice was raised to make itself heard over the men's booming tones. Suzanne stood unnoticed for a moment in the doorway. Peter was taller than his brother Dan, but only by an inch or two. His build was sturdier, as if he was well fed on board the ships in which he travelled the world.

When they saw her in the doorway, all talking stopped, then Peter exclaimed, 'Hey there, who are you?'

'Don't fall for his line,' Dan warned cheerfully, dishing up the meal. 'He's developed a lightning-quick approach. He never has much time on leave,' he dodged his brother's playfully thrusting fist, 'so he has to work fast on the female of the species.'

Suzanne laughed, but her eyes did not light up.

'What's wrong, little girl?' Peter pursued. 'You in mourning, or something?'

'Yes, she's lost her heart,' Maggie quipped, 'and not to you, Pete. Got it?' She lifted Suzanne's left hand. 'So don't "little girl" her.'

'Married?' asked the unquenchable Peter. 'That's no barrier these days. Dan, why didn't you tell me you'd got me a blind date? I'd have put on my best clothes!'

The meal revived Suzanne's spirits to a certain level, sufficient to laugh at jokes and almost clear her plate, to Dan's satisfaction.

'You're good at cooking, Dan,' she complimented

him. She could not add the words that were in her mind, Almost as good as my husband. That would have widened Maggie's eyes and had her boy-friend's brother staring. It seemed he was convinced that her husband had recently divorced her, hence her lack of animation.

'He is good,' Maggie agreed, winding her arm round Dan's neck. 'When we're married, he can take over the kitchen, as far as I'm concerned. I think,' she added as she cleared away, 'I'll send him to cookery classes at the local college.'

There was general laughter at this statement and Suzanne, fearing being left alone with Peter, whose ebullient manner was drawing more from her in response than she really had to give, offered to help Maggie bring in the second course.

The evening passed pleasantly with music and coffee and yet more banter between the men. Suzanne tolerated Peter's hand holding hers as they shared the couch, while Dan and Maggie shared an armchair. She knew he would not take her tolerance as a sign of encouragement, for he seemed to have got the message at last that she was just not on offer.

Peter asked if he could take her home. Having left her car in the yard at the rear of the shop, she was relying on Maggie to take her back there at the end of the evening to collect it.

'Go on, dear, be tempted,' Maggie urged. 'Your car will be quite safe where it is until the morning. I'll call for you then and take you to work. Okay? Right, Peter, you've got yourself a passenger.'

Suzanne had been looking bewilderedly from one to the other. Now she shook her head and smiled. 'You're all talking much too fast for my tired old brain. How do I stand now as far as getting home's concerned?'

'You don't stand,' Peter pointed out. 'You sit— beside me in my car. Right, Maggie. Where's her coat before she changes her mind?'

Suzanne thanked Maggie for giving her such a happy evening.

'You deserved the break, Suzanne. I hope it's helped
you put things in a better perspective.'

'Well, let's say it's helped. See you tomorrow.
Goodnight, Dan.'

He insisted on kissing her—on her cheeks, as Maggie
demanded, pretending to be fierce. Suzanne left her
friend's house with laughter on her lips, and this time it
reached her eyes.

'It's not far,' Suzanne told Peter as he drove along
the dark and narrow country lanes.

'Maggie lives too near to you,' he complained, his
tone simulating annoyance.

Suzanne laughed but could find nothing to say.

'You've only been half with us this evening, haven't
you?' Peter commented with a sideways glance. 'He must
be something, this husband of yours.'

It was a while before she could bring herself to speak.
'Yes, he is that,' she answered at last. 'But——'

'I knew there'd be a "but",' Peter interrupted. 'There
always is. Nothing ever seems to run smoothly in this
life. That's why I fight shy of legal involvements.' His
glance came her way again. 'I didn't say emotional. I'm
beginning to get the feeling that I wish you were legally
free, too.'

Wait long enough, Suzanne thought with bitterness,
and I might be just that, one way or another.

'It's a long story,' was all she said as, at her direction,
he turned into the driveway and braked.

'Nice place you have here. Rich, is he, this husband
of yours?'

'Certainly not rich, but he gets by.'

' "He", not "we"?'

Suzanne kept her eyes on the darkened house. Had
they gone to bed? Or were they still dining and dancing?

'I can see you're not with me.' Peter opened his door and
walked round to let her out of his car. She thanked him and
would have walked away had he not detained her.

'A kiss, little Suzie?' he asked in such an appealing
tone, she laughed.

'Well, maybe,' she pretended to consider, 'just one, a little one.'

The 'little kiss' turned into a long one. When it started to deepen, Suzanne stiffened, and he let her go reluctantly. 'Mm, it was good renewing my acquaintance with a full-bodied female again. I meant that,' he added hastily, 'in the sense that a wine is full-bodied. Get me?'

Suzanne laughed again. 'I must go in. Have a good leave,' she called, lifting her hand.

'I'd have an even better one if I could spend it with you,' he called back. Then he drove away, his brake lights flashing 'goodnight'.

Although the house had appeared to be in darkness, Suzanne heard a movement from upstairs. She froze, her back to the door. Ross, come to interrogate her? Ross with Tania, in her apartment? The landing light was switched on.

It was Tania alone who stood at the top of the stairs, smiling down.

'Had a pleasant evening?' Tania asked. Just as if she was the woman of the house, Suzanne thought, instead of me.

'Very pleasant, thank you.'

'Who was your escort? An old friend, by the way he kissed you.'

Suzanne compressed her lips to keep in the anger. Ignoring the question, she asked, 'Where's Ross?'

'He's staying in London overnight. Some important guests to entertain, then tomorrow he has discussions with them. Didn't he tell you?'

She may seem innocuous, Suzanne fumed, but there's sting in the tail of almost everything she says to me.

'I keep forgetting to—to ask his movements.'

'Well, it's a good thing you've got friends in the neighbourhood to keep you company when you're lonely, isn't it?'

Was the woman being deliberately bitchy? Suzanne raged silently.

'A very good thing.' She made for the living-room. 'Goodnight, Tania.'

' 'Bye, Suzanne.' Tania turned away and made for her apartment.

After work next day, Suzanne was greeted by silence as she entered the hallway. She was accustomed by now, she told herself, to the negative welcome of an empty house.

Feeling no immediate urge to eat, she went into the living-room and dropped tiredly into an armchair. There was the sensation in her mind of someone who had reached a crossroads and did not know which route to take.

A sound alerted her. She listened, then swung her head to the door. Ross stood there, shirt partly unbuttoned, slacks casual, hands in his pockets. Hadn't he been to work?

'What are you doing here at this time?' Suzanne asked, the shock of his unexpected presence sharpening her tone.

'I gave myself an hour or two off—I had some pressing business to attend to at home. I was upstairs when you came in.'

Suzanne frowned. 'I see,' she replied, although she did not. 'Is Tania upstairs, too?'

'Tania's gone. I came to collect her this morning and took her back to London.'

'She's left?' Suzanne would have cried for joy if she hadn't already been crying inside.

Ross nodded and strolled across to face her. His breadth and height still daunted her, the hardness of the man within equalling that of the hard muscularity of his body. It was his inner hardness that made her despair. Not even by a centimetre had he softened towards her, not even when he had made passionate love, lying with her afterwards intertwined in mind as well as body.

His jaw jutted, forcing his long-boned facial structure to stretch his strangely-drawn skin. 'You enjoyed your evening?' His tone revealed a disconcerting interest.

'Quite a lot, thank you.' In between periods of not enjoying it, she added to herself. 'It was—homely, for want of a better word.'

'Homely?' The dark brows pushed upwards. 'So the Harringdon family are still cherishing the hope that you'll join them one day as their daughter-in-law?'

'*Harringdon* family?' Her frown had deepened. 'What have they got to do with how I spent yesterday evening?'

'So Miles Harringdon took you home, did he? Then brought you back, quite late, I was told. After which he gave you a passionate goodnight kiss.'

'He did?' Suzanne sat forward, every muscle tense. 'That's news to me. Your informer was wrong. If she'd known better, she would have recognised that the car didn't belong to Miles.'

'So whose car was it?'

Settling back in the chair, she smiled up at him. It was meant to provoke, as were her words. 'His name is Peter, and he's on leave from his ship. He's about a year younger than I am.'

Her smile remained steady, her brown eyes deepening as they returned his cold stare. She was not smiling inside. 'He's Dan's brother,' she explained into the silence. 'Dan, in case you don't know, is Maggie's fiancé. They're getting married soon, she told me today. Last night Peter made up a foursome, at Maggie's house.' She forced her smile to broaden. 'I really enjoyed myself.'

With an action so swift she cried out in fear, Ross caught a handful of her dress and hoisted her up from the armchair, forcing her to stand so close to him she could feel his breath. She struggled vainly to free her dress from his grasp.

'So you let a complete stranger kiss you as if he were your lover.'

Her eyes flared, daring his. 'Maybe he is my lover. If he was, you wouldn't care——'

The back of his hand hit her cheek with such a stinging blow, her breath choked on a gasp. He released her and she dropped back into the chair. With her hands over her face, she struggled for composure, controlling the welling tears.

'You're wrong, wrong about everything,' she told him brokenly. 'And if you want to know why I went to Maggie's for a meal last night,' her voice lowered, 'it was because I simply couldn't face coming back home again. I couldn't face Tania's possessiveness towards you, I couldn't face your constant hostility towards me.'

With a smothered curse, Ross dropped beside her and pulled her round. His mouth was twisted, not with scorn but a kind of pain. 'My God, Suzanne, if you knew . . .'

There was the sound of car tyres on the driveway. Had Tania come back? Suzanne rushed to the window. 'It's my parents, come to visit us!' She was out of the door before Ross could stop her.

Her mother was at the wheel, her father climbing out of the car. 'Mum, it's good to see you! Are you coming in?'

Cynthia's smile was tentative, lacking confidence. 'Your father is, dear. I won't.'

'Father?' He was standing beside her. He did not smile. He carried a briefcase, and he looked ill at ease. Suzanne was puzzled and anxious. He started to move slowly towards the house.

Suzanne knew she would have to act the go-between. If he and Ross were left alone, heaven knew what trouble would follow, how much ill-feeling would be excavated from under layers of past constraints.

'Mother, what does Father want with Ross?'

Cynthia pushed her head through the window opening. 'He'll tell you, I expect. Suzanne,' she put her hand on her daughter's which gripped the lowered window, 'your father's not all bad. I love him, dear, otherwise I wouldn't have stayed with him all these difficult years.'

For this, she thought again with a bitterness she could not lose, I gave up my chance of happiness.

'I had to drive here,' her mother went on, 'because he was too nervous—yes, I mean nervous—to drive. I know you won't believe me.'

'I believe you, Mum. I'm starting to believe a lot of things about—about people that I didn't believe before.'

She looked back and found her father waiting patiently on the doorstep. The door had swung almost closed. Her father—patient!

'Suzanne,' Cynthia claimed her daughter's attention, 'whatever you do, don't let Ross go. He's a good man.'

'But, Mum, he's got someone else. He might divorce me—he said so.'

Cynthia started to turn the car. 'Fight for him,' she called as she completed the turn, 'with everything you've got.'

'Aren't you going to let me in?' Lucas growled as his daughter reached him. 'How much longer have I got to stand on the doorstep of this house?'

'Come in, come in, Father. You haven't been here before, have you?' The words were tumbling out in a wild cascade. 'I'll get Ross. It was him you came to see, wasn't it, not me. You wouldn't come to see me——'

'Mr Cannon?' Ross spoke from behind her. He had put on a tie, combed his hair. Why was he so formal with her father? Why couldn't he—why couldn't they both—relax?

Lucas gave a cursory glance around the living-room, noting the boldly-patterned carpet, the expensive furnishings, the glass-panelled dining area.

'Sit down, Father. Ross——?' Her worried frown asked him, Why aren't you playing host? 'I don't know whether you'd like a drink, Father?'

'I never mix business with pleasure.' He chose the couch, Suzanne an armchair.

'It's approaching the weekend, Mr Cannon,' Ross responded with a faint smile. 'Winding down time. I never tackle a business problem on a Friday afternoon. Except, of course, in exceptional circumstances.'

Lucas looked up at the younger man. 'This is exceptional. I've come to ask you for more money.'

Ross's eyes narrowed as they stared down at his wife.

'What do you know about this?'

Suzanne felt the impact of her father's statement like a brick hitting her head. Her face lost its colour. 'Nothing, I swear.'

'She knows nothing about this. Think I'd tell *her*?'

Involuntarily, Suzanne winced. As a reaction, it was purely instinctive, left over, as she now understood, from her childhood. All the same, the dismissal of her by her father as an unthinking, unreasoning human being still had the power to hurt.

Ross pushed his hands into his slacks pockets. His head was thrown slightly back, his whole attitude one of belligerence. 'So you want more money out of me, Mr Cannon. Where the hell do you think I'm going to get it from?'

'I don't know your financial circumstances,' Lucas blustered. 'From where you got the other lot of money, I suppose. Bank loan, wasn't it?'

'You think I can extend it on demand, just like that?' Ross clicked his fingers.

'Why,' Lucas snapped, 'isn't your credit standing as high as you boasted it was? Are your bankers threatening to call in their first loan to you?' He spoke as if the whole idea amused him.

'Maybe I just don't want to throw good money after bad. If you need more money, you must have mishandled the money I loaned you.'

'It's the times, isn't it? They're hard on businessmen like me. Aren't you businessman enough yourself to know that? Or have you got your head in the academic clouds all the time?'

'There are no academic clouds to get lost in, in the African bush, Mr Cannon.' He sat at last, his strong thighs pushing at the taut material of his slacks. His still-tanned arms stretched along the arms of the chair, the dark hairs on them reminding Suzanne of the darker mat of hair on his chest.

Her head turned away quickly as emotion clouded her vision. Lucas watched him closely, like prey watching, wondering which way to dodge when the predator made its next move.

'There may be an obstacle in the way of my lending you even more money. An obstacle like a divorce, for instance.' His hooded gaze bruised Suzanne's pale face.

'What divorce?' Lucas demanded, his face turning almost as white as his daughter's. 'She can't divorce you, not now. Miles Harringdon's got himself nearly engaged to another girl.'

A flicker of amusement loosened Ross's tight lips. 'Glad to hear his heart wasn't too badly broken by losing your daughter.'

'What do you mean, "my daughter"? She's your wife!'

Ross took one second to get to his feet. 'Full circle. Your permission to our marriage at last.' His eyes were hard as granite. 'Over seven long years it's taken for you to give your consent. Ironic, isn't it, when there's talk of divorce again.'

'What divorce?' Lucas asked for a second time, his voice a hoarse whisper.

Suzanne got to her feet, confronting Ross. 'My husband has another woman, Father,' she said, tones clear and brittle. 'She's been staying here. She's gone now, but the love affair he had with her while they were together in Africa isn't over.'

Ross folded his arms slowly, lowering his head menacingly. 'And my wife's faithfulness to me is in grave doubt. It seems she's taken a lover, and under my very nose, too. So, Mr Cannon,' he turned to Lucas, 'we're quits. Irretrievable breakdown of marriage without any doubt, wouldn't you say?'

Lucas tried to get to his feet, but it seemed he hadn't the strength. He clutched at the pile of papers on his lap, and Suzanne noticed with concern that her father's hands were shaking. From among the debris of her shattered dreams, she reached out in her mind to offer pity to her proud, dogmatic father.

Lucas gazed, stupefied, from one to the other. 'Look, son,' he said at last, 'couldn't you try again? She'd break her heart now if you left her a second time.'

'You mean,' Ross hit back, 'you would break your——' His eyes swung to those of his wife, hers to his. 'Son', Lucas had said.

'I called you "son".' Lucas spoke gruffly and with wonder.

There was a long silence. Ross stared at the carpet, Suzanne at her father. 'The son you've never had,' she said with a break in her voice, 'but have always wanted.'

Lucas pushed away the papers and tried again to get to his feet. Suzanne moved to help him, and he did not push her hand away. He picked up his briefcase, looked first at one, then the other. His legs, as he went to the door, seemed just a little weak.

'Father, I'll give you a lift.'

He dismissed the offer with a movement of his hand. Suzanne opened the front door and watched him walk through. 'Cynthia will be waiting outside,' he said. 'She wouldn't come in.'

Watching the short, stout figure walk slowly down the drive, she knew that Ross was watching, too, beside her.

He went towards the coat stand, raked in his jacket pocket and withdrew a bunch of car keys. Then he passed her with a cool, 'Excuse me,' and strode across the driveway to get into a car—her car. She remembered that he had her duplicate set of keys. Wondering why he was not using his own larger car, she saw with a frown that he had swung hers round and was racing down the drive to the main entrance.

Where had he gone? she wondered unhappily. To go after Tania, wherever she was, and spend yet another night with her? A surge of anger swept through her at the man who could treat his father-in-law so callously, announcing almost in the same breath that he would be seeking a divorce which would free him not only from her, his wife, but from the loan which probably, albatross-like, hung round his neck.

Well, she wouldn't wait to be pushed out of Ross's

life. She would walk out and stay out, this time for ever. Running up the stairs, she arrived breathless in her bedroom. Pulling out all the suitcases she could find, she began throwing in her clothes and every other possession of hers she could lay her hands on.

Twenty minutes later, one case was full to overflowing, while a second was on the way to that state. The fury which had catapulted her up the stairs and had been the driving force behind her movements ever since was still drumming in her ears when her side-glance told her of the presence of the man who blocked the doorway.

Under his frigid scrutiny, her movements slowed down but did not stop.

'What do you think you're doing?' he asked curtly.

'Packing, leaving, getting out before you humble my pride like you did my father's and tell me to get out. That's what I'm doing.'

In three strides he was beside the bed. He took the overflowing suitcase and upturned it, emptying the contents on to the covers. The other case received the same treatment.

'Why, you——' She hit out, but he caught her wrists, stilling their flailing action with an agonising grip. Tears of frustration filtered from behind her eyes. 'How could you do that to my father? The help you gave him with one hand you're going to take away with the other. He came to you humbled—you must have seen his shaking hands—yet you deliberately trod on his pride. He never would have come begging again if he hadn't been desperate.'

His eyebrows arched. 'What have I done to your father?'

'Not only have you refused to lend him more money, you're going to demand repayment of the loan you've already given him.'

Would she ever shake this man's coolness?

'How did you reach that conclusion?'

'If—if you'll let go of my wrists, I'll tell you.' At once

he did so, watching, seemingly unmoved, as she tried to massage away the pain.

'You're going to divorce me and marry Tania—that's what you told him.'

'Did I mention Tania's name?'

'You didn't have to. I know she's your woman, you told me so. Tania or not, if you divorce me, it means you don't need me here as a surety any more, because you will have forced my father into even deeper trouble by making him repay the original loan.'

He folded his arms, his steady, ice-cold gaze making her shiver. 'You really think I'm that kind of a man?'

'You think I'm the kind of woman who'd take a lover—not only that, but on sight, like a—like a sleep-around.' His gaze was steady, waiting. 'Ross,' her voice was strained now, 'if I ask Maggie to tell you I only met Dan's brother Peter last night and that all that happened when he brought me home was that he kissed me, would you believe her?' Nothing would stop her now. She would tell him everything. 'I've never taken a lover, not once through all those years—those lonely years.'

When he spoke, the harshness that edged his voice told her that he felt no forgiveness, despite her honesty with him about her private life.

'Then why did you agree to marry Harringdon? The whole engagement was a ridiculous pretence, and you knew it.'

'For my father's sake,' she answered simply. 'He desperately needed the money he thought the engagement would bring. I hadn't heard from you once since you walked away that day. I thought you'd forgotten me, found another woman more sophisticated than the wife in her teens you left behind.'

It was difficult to go on, especially in the face of his seeming intractability, but she persisted. 'I gave up hope. After——' she needed to steady her voice, 'after you, I knew no other man would even begin to make me love him. So,' she shrugged, 'I thought I might as well start divorce proceedings and marry Miles, self-effacing, undemanding Miles. But,' she added in a whisper, 'that was before you came back.'

There was a long pause. Ross went to the window and stared out.

'Why did you take Tania as your mistress?' Suzanne's voice rose. The tension which his refusal to see her point of view was causing was telling on her. 'How could you, Ross, how could you?'

'How could I indeed!' He was standing rigidly in front of her now. 'Days, months, years I endured without you beside me. I suffered agonies because I wanted and needed a woman, not just any woman, only you.'

He jerked her chin round and upward to make her look at him. 'In the end, it had to be any woman. I'm a realist. And I'm not made of the stuff that can accept celibacy as a way of life. Nor am I given to fantasising my needs away. But—this above all—I wanted *my* woman there, yet I couldn't have her. Now do you see what you did to me?'

He released her chin, yet she remained gazing up at him, boldly, defiantly. 'I was so young, Ross. I dared not leave my mother to my father's mercies—or so I thought in those days. I've learnt since that my sacrifice was unnecessary. Nothing, but nothing, would tear my mother from my father's side. She loves him, she keeps telling me. I didn't know that then. How *was* I to know, at only seventeen?'

Still there was cold anger in Ross's eyes as he stared back at her, as if the memories continued to torment him. 'I imagined you with other men, I tortured myself thinking you'd forgotten me.'

'Why didn't you ever come back, Ross?' she asked.

'More than once I almost gave up the job and came home. But I carried a nightmare picture in my mind— of travelling all that way only to find you looking at me with blank eyes and asking, who are you? then finding the door slammed in my face. By you.'

Her heart was pounding with the building tension.

When would his story end, and when would she be released from the anguish of listening to him telling her of how his love for her had died?

'So I turned to Tania,' he said. 'She talked my language, and she was not unattractive, so we went around together.'

'And slept together.'

'It didn't work. It didn't for her, either. She was mourning the loss of her fiancé. He'd found someone else. We thought we'd find solace together, but my heart wasn't in it. I was always thinking of you—you, my wife. I'm not the kind to commit adultery with a counterfeit smile on my face and murmuring false words of love. In the end, I channelled my sexual energies into hard, physical work. I tried my damnedest to get you out of my system, but I couldn't.'

He reached out and pulled her to her feet. 'And right now, I want you back there, circulating in my blood,' she was against him now, 'racing through my veins, bringing me back to life.'

With one movement, he cleared the bed of her clothes. Then he urged her backwards and down on to it. 'God, you don't know what life was like without you there. I was only half alive. I want you now, do you understand?'

Suzanne nodded, her eyes catching fire from his. He was unfastening her dress, kissing each area of throbbing flesh as it was revealed, lingering long and hungrily at the hardening point of each breast.

Even as he caressed her with his lips and hands and in the midst of her growing ecstasy, she peeled the shirt from his shoulders. Then there were no barriers to keep them apart and her arms lifted and locked round his neck, feeling the ripple of muscle as he moved across her.

Her fingers skimmed his back, moulding, with curled hands the muscles of his shoulders. His lips said against hers, 'Know what I missed most when we were apart? Your sparkling eyes, your smile as I possessed you. It was not only the physical satisfaction you gave to me so generously, it was the love we shared in the act of love itself.'

'I'm here now, Ross,' she whispered, 'and loving you more perhaps than even at the start. And Ross,' she strained against him, 'I want you, too. I need you, I've needed you for so many years.'

He took her then and time ceased to exist. Life was the throb of their pulses, the drumming of their heart-beats, the melting of them into one.

Later, when the glow was fading a little, they were still entwined. 'Hallo again,' he whispered against her ear. Suzanne smilingly murmured the same words back. It was as though the six lost years had never been.

Her voice came softly out of the stillness. 'Where did Tania go to, darling, when she left here?'

'Back to her fiancé.'

Suzanne's head lifted. 'You didn't tell me she was engaged!'

'Re-engaged. When she and her fiancé broke up, he married another woman, but it didn't work. Now he's free again, and Tania is back with him. They're going to get married.'

'If only I'd known! I would have been much nicer to her.'

'She was aware of that and accepted your barbed comments with good grace.' He raised himself on to his elbow and smiled down at her.

'You let me go on insulting her,' she stormed, her eyes flashing.

'Go on being angry,' he commented lazily, running a finger across her brow, 'it makes you look so beautiful.'

She seized his hand and tried to bite the finger. He turned the tables and nipped her knuckles. 'You never told me why you bought Maggie's shop,' she accused.

'For you. Who else would I have in mind? It was your work, you obviously loved it, the way you spent your time making things to sell in it. It's a gift from me to you, my darling.'

Suzanne looked up at him with mischief in her gaze. 'Is there any way I can thank you, kind sir?'

His narrowed eyes skimmed her body from head to foot. 'One very special way. Shall I demonstrate?'

She dived for the cover, which had become dislodged and fallen to the ground, and Ross allowed her to pull it across them.

'Nor did you tell me,' she said slowly, 'how you came to be a millionaire—all this money you've been throwing around.'

'Ah, now that's a long story.' His eyes twinkled.

He was, she thought with wonder, the Ross she had married. He had turned from stone to the human state. Had she, after all, held the key within herself, yet had not even realised it? In a few seconds, she felt she had become immeasurably wiser and older. Yet in her heart she was young again, as young as she had been in that first wonderful year.

'To tell you that tale,' Ross reached out, 'I must have you here in my arms. Come close to me, my love. No, closer still, so I can feel your heartbeat and you feel mine.'

She curled herself round him, mumbling against the soft chest hairs, 'Is that close enough? You couldn't get a piece of spun silk between us now.'

'It will do,' he conceded, 'for the moment. Now, let's begin.' He demanded a kiss and got one. 'It was all a long time ago.'

Her body snuggled into the hardness of him as she listened attentively.

'It all began when my rich grandfather, who was, if anything, even more awkward than your father,' she smiled up at him, 'refused to acknowledge the girl my mother—whom my father had married. She was too poor for my father, he said, wouldn't know how to live up to the family's weatlh. When my father died, my grandfather sent for me.'

'Not for your mother?'

'Not for her, for me. She took me there, of course,

but he still wouldn't see her. I was about seven and hardly understood a word of what was going on around me. He told me he intended leaving me his fortune in trust for when I was a man, which, he said, was at the age of twenty-five. It was a great deal of money, my darling.'

Suzanne looked up at him with large eyes. 'You never told me.'

'My grandfather had sworn me to secrecy. I was to tell no one, he said. He would give the lawyers all the necessary instructions, and that as soon as I left his house—to me it was a kind of palace—I was to forget everything he told me. I very nearly did, except that I immediately told my mother, thus going against my grandfather's wishes. I always told my mother everything.'

'Of course,' she agreed, nodding her head against his upper arm until he told her she was beginning to drive him crazy. She laughed at this, but stopped at once.

'When I was almost twenty-four, as you know, we married. A few weeks after we parted—after only a year together—I inherited that fortune. My love,' he tipped her face and kissed her throat, 'the world would have been at our feet.'

'I'm sorry,' she gazed into his faintly reprimanding eyes, 'what more can I say? It wasn't because I didn't love you.'

'And I thought it was. I hardly touched the money. Without you to share it with me, I lost interest in it. So what did I do? I worked madly, making even more money to add to it.'

Suzanne made small circles round his shoulder, having nothing to say in reply.

'When I went out in your car this evening, I drove like mad to catch your parents before they left. I caught them in their car, still talking at the kerb. Your mother got into the back of the car, I took her place in the front.'

Suzanne lifted her head expectantly. 'Well?' she asked.

'I'm now part of your father's company, my darling. I told him that the money I'd lent him was a gift and that the extra money would come from my buying a stake in the business and becoming a director.'

'Ross, oh, Ross!' Her hands gripped his arms and she could not hold back the tears of happiness. 'You're good, so good. My mother called you a good man.'

'And your father called me "son". It was enough, my love. He had accepted me as my grandfather never once accepted my mother. I'd become part of the Cannon company.'

'Now you're truly one of the family,' she added, her voice thick.

Ross turned her towards him. 'That nursery, Mrs Beckett, which you so acidly told me would be filled by a woman other than my wife. You and I are going to fill it——'

'*Fill* it?' she gasped.

'Let's say with two—or maybe by "mistake"—three offspring. That should keep you busy for a long time to come.'

There was a rumbling noise and Suzanne glanced down with surprise at her stomach. 'I'm hungry,' she said. 'We haven't had our evening meal.'

'Oh no,' he grabbed her, pulling her on to him, 'not yet. I'm hungry too, not for food, but for you. Come here, mother-to-be of my children. I give you warning. I intend to make love—passionate, *loving* love—to you that will satisfy you so much, you won't need to eat until morning.'

He rolled her back and stroked and caressed. 'My love,' he muttered against her softness, 'oh, my love, I'll never let you go again. I'll bind you to me with bonds so secure you'll never be able to break away from me.'

'I'll never want to, Ross,' she whispered. 'Every part of me is yours from now until time ends.'

Then she was gathered into him, and the world ceased to matter.

# ROMANCE

# Variety is the spice of romance

Each month, Mills & Boon publish new romances. New stories about people falling in love. A world of variety in romance – from the best writers in the romantic world. Choose from these titles in February.

**HIDDEN LOVE** Carole Mortimer
**FLIGHT OF THE GOLDEN HAWK** Sheila Strutt
**THE SILVER CASKET** Patricia Lake
**DEADLY ANGEL** Sarah Holland
**FLYING HIGH** Sally Wentworth
**TEMPTED TO LOVE** Flora Kidd
**WEB OF SILK** Yvonne Whittal
**ESCAPE FROM DESIRE** Penny Jordan
**HUNTER'S MOON** Margaret Way
**NO OTHER MAN** Lilian Peake
**VALENTINE'S DAY** Jayne Bauling
**STAG AT BAY** Victoria Gordon

On sale where you buy paperbacks. If you require further information or have any difficulty obtaining them, write to: Mills & Boon Reader Service, PO Box 236, Thornton Road, Croydon, Surrey CR9 3RU, England.

# Mills & Boon

the rose of romance

# ROMANCE

# Next month's romances from Mills & Boon

Each month, you can choose from a world of variety in romance with Mills & Boon. These are the new titles to look out for next month.

**LORD OF THE LAND** Margaret Rome
**CALL UP THE STORM** Jane Donnelly
**BETRAYAL** Charlotte Lamb
**THE DEVIL'S ADVOCATE** Vanessa James
**VISION OF LOVE** Elizabeth Graham
**CHAINS OF GOLD** Yvonne Whittal
**CLOUDED RAPTURE** Margaret Pargeter
**THE FLAWED MARRIAGE** Penny Jordan
**MIDSUMMER STAR** Betty Neels
**LOVE'S ONLY DECEPTION** Carole Mortimer
**PASSIONATE ENEMIES** Kathryn Cranmer
**SEA LIGHTNING** Linda Harrel

Buy them from your usual paperback stockist, or write to: Mills & Boon Reader Service, P.O. Box 236, Thornton Rd, Croydon, Surrey CR9 3RU, England. Readers in South Africa-write to: Mills & Boon Reader Service of Southern Africa, Private Bag X3010, Randburg, 2125.

## Mills & Boon
the rose of romance

# Best Seller Romances

# These best loved romances are back

Mills & Boon Best Seller Romances are the love stories that have proved particularly popular with our readers. These are the titles to look out for this month.

**AVENGING ANGEL** Helen Bianchin
**A GIFT FOR A LION** Sara Craven
**FIESTA SAN ANTONIO** Janet Dailey
**PRINCE FOR SALE** Rachel Lindsay
**ALIEN WIFE** Anne Mather
**THE LOVE BATTLE** Violet Winspear

Buy them from your usual paperback stockist, or write to: Mills & Boon Reader Service, P.O. Box 236, Thornton Rd, Croydon, Surrey CR9 3RU, England. Readers in South Africa-write to: Mills & Boon Reader Service of Southern Africa, Private Bag X3010, Randburg, 2125.

# Mills & Boon
### the rose of romance

# FREE-an exclusive Anne Mather title, MELTING FIRE

At Mills & Boon we value very highly the opinion of our readers. What you tell us about what you like in romantic reading is important to us.

So if you will tell us which Mills & Boon romance you have most enjoyed reading lately, we will send you a copy of MELTING FIRE by Anne Mather – absolutely FREE.

There are no snags, no hidden charges. It's absolutely FREE.

Just send us your answer to our question, and help us to bring you the best in romantic reading.

CLAIM YOUR FREE BOOK NOW

Simply fill in details below, cut out and post to: Mills & Boon Reader Service, FREEPOST, P.O. Box 236, Croydon, Surrey CR9 9EL.

The Mills & Boon story I have most enjoyed during the past 6 months is:

TITLE _____

AUTHOR_____ BLOCK LETTERS, PLEASE

NAME (Mrs/Miss) _____ EP4

ADDRESS _____

_____

_____ POST CODE _____

Offer restricted to ONE Free Book a year per household. Applies only in U.K. and Eire.
CUT OUT AND POST TODAY – NO STAMP NEEDED.

## Mills & Boon
### the rose of romance